The Girl with the Emerald Brooch

Growing up:
1954 - 1965

Bittersweet times — recalled with love.

Jacqueline Creek

J. R. Nicholls

Published by
J. R. Nicholls
Denby Dale HD8 8RT

This paperback edition first published 2016

ISBN: 978-1-911347-00-2

1 3 5 7 9 10 8 6 4 2

Printed and bound in Great Britain by
D&M Heritage Press, Huddersfield HD2 1YE

For John and Dave, with all my love.

Prologue

The Lost Streets of Owlerton: Tizer Women

I lived in Sheffield just along the road from where Tizer was made and bottled.

TIZER is a non-alcoholic drink launched in 1924, which became very popular during the forties and fifties. During the Second World War, many women had to work in the factories, doing the work of the men who had joined the armed forces.

Much of the work was heavy, especially in the steelworks, but a bottling plant was hard work too. The glass bottles were large, thick and heavy and so were the solid wooden crates, which each housed twelve bottles.

When the war ended a lot of women were still necessary in the factories, as the returning men were needed to re-build the country.

I, along with other children of this era, was afraid of these heavy-set red-faced women, and would wait by the factory gates for them to finish their shifts. As soon as the gates opened and we could hear the sound of their clogs, we would run along the pavement ahead of them shouting 'The Tizer Women are coming.'

The terraced streets of Owlerton have now disappeared, bulldozed when the A61 was widened into a dual carriageway. Tanfield Road, where I lived, still exists, but there are no houses now – just a couple of motor garages and a second hand car dealership.

Do the people working there now ever stop to wonder about the thriving community that once lived in Owlerton?

This poem is in memory of the women who worked long hours at 'Pickup's' on Penistone Road, Owlerton, Sheffield.

TIZER WOMEN

Mothers, daughters, sisters, aunts,
With turbaned heads – crowns of their class…
Spew through the factory gates at close of shift.
Shoulders slumped from years of toil,
Their forearms crossed like mutton legs
Held tight against their heaving chests,
And red-raw hands shoved in armpits.

Leather aprons stained and wet
Bound around such hefty thighs,
Buxom girths sway with each stride,
And steel-capped clogs spark every flag.
Haggard, hardened, old before time.
Skin the colour of the grimy brick streets,
Heavy-eyed they head for home…

Where bailiffs prowl. And more demands.
Sick children cry, hungry husbands shout,
Aged parents moan…of heatless fires
And food-less shelves. An empty purse
Such poor rewards for labours past
They can but hope…for a jug of 'mild'…
And a pack of 'Wood's' on Friday.

'It was the only gift he gave me apart from you.'

Mum sat in the nursing chair by the side of the fireplace and held the brooch in the palm of her hand. She was trying to tell me something.

I was ten years old. I sat opposite her in Dad's chair, nursing my four-week-old brother. He needed a feed and made sure we knew. I glanced across at the green, jewelled brooch in the palm of her hand, while gently shushing the bawling infant.

The jewels set into the brooch weren't bright and shining like the ones the Queen wore. I didn't like it much.

'Here Mum, take Ian while I make his bottle.' I placed the baby in her lap and busied myself behind her, in the corner of the kitchen where the sink and the two-ring gas burner stood.

Having just spent the last three months in hospital with toxaemia, which had also affected the baby, Mum couldn't breastfeed Ian. At the age of forty-one, he was her third child. Everyone said how lucky she and the infant were to be alive, thanks to the medical ministrations of 1954.

I mixed Ian's formula and took a new teat out of the packet, squeezed the end and decided it needed another hole. Taking a needle from the pincushion on the mantelshelf, I held it under the gas flame for a few seconds. I pierced the teat and secured it on the bottle. Stepping onto the small stool in front of the stove, I placed it in a pan of boiling water to heat.

I looked across at Mum and nibbled my fingernails while she

couldn't see me. I saw that the beautiful auburn waves of hair she'd been so proud of were dull and flat.

Allowed time off from school, and with the help of Mum's sister Doris, I managed to look after Mum, my five-year-old sister Josie, and Dad. I didn't realise at the time, but he was getting quite elderly.

'It's such a shame,' my teacher had told Dad, the day before Mum came out of hospital. 'Jacqueline's such a bright girl – always in the top three, and this is her scholarship year. There must be an alternative.'

She must have talked to the school board inspector too. A letter had arrived, asking my parents to attend a meeting, but they didn't go.

I wanted to pass my scholarship and become a doctor, a surgeon actually, and find out what made people ill.

I'd practised on my fingers with a fine needle and a single strand of embroidery silk, easing the needle through the thick top layer of skin on my finger pads and sewing a continuous thread through all four fingers. I did it to Josie once when we were playing doctors and nurses. Painting a red line on her middle finger pad, I sewed over it with tiny stitches. She showed it to her friends, and then all the kids who lived in the street were at our door. Some wanted to see how I did it, others wanted the experience.

'Stop it. Now,' Mum had snapped.

'Being a doctor isn't for the likes of us, love.' Dad had agreed.

'But Mum used to be a nurse,' I replied. 'There can't be that much difference.'

'There was a war on – they took anybody.'

'Well, thanks, Charlie.' Mum cut in. 'Your Dad's right though, love, doctoring isn't for the likes of us.'

'Why? If I pass my exams, then what's to stop me?'

'She's getting too many ideas above her station.' Dad looked across at Mum, and dismissed the subject by lighting his pipe.

'It's not as simple as that,' she said, looking at me and then back at Dad, who was sitting in his chair, filling the room with smoke.

* * * *

I came back to the present, squirted a few drops of milk onto the inside of my wrist to test it, and handed the bottle to Mum. She looked ill and frail as she sat feeding the quietened child. I noticed the brooch, now on the hearth beside her chair. What was she trying to tell me?

The coal shifted in the grate, sending sparks flying towards the nappies hanging on the fireguard. I pulled the fireguard away and thrust the poker into the fire to settle it. A pile of ash and cinders fell into the bottom of the grate, sending a cloud of dust into the air.

The huge black fireplace had a large oven and a recess to one side which housed the sink and gas hob. On the other side was a floor-to-ceiling cupboard, built into the recess, which aired the sheets and towels, and warmed Ian's baby clothes. The bottom of the cupboard stored our shoes and Wellingtons, along with old newspapers, empty sugar bags and washing soda boxes for making coal-slack logs.

'I think it needs some more coal, love,' she said, with a shudder. 'And take note how much is left.'

I made my way to the coal stack beneath the grate in the cellar, carefully walking along the row of brick stepping stones. I scooped a heaped shovel full of slack and coal, drained off the black water and balanced my way back, along the bricks and up the stone steps. Tipping the coal into the fire caused more sparks and crackling. When it settled, I replaced the fireguard and turned the nappies.

'There's about a bag full left.' I said. I and went over to the sink, filled the kettle and put it on to boil. I looked at the list on the back of the cupboard door. 'He's due in the street next week.'

'How much is in the tin?' she asked, without turning.

I reached up onto the mantelshelf, took down the Sharp's toffee tin, and looked inside. A ten-shilling note, half a crown, a two-shilling piece, six shillings and a sixpence.

'Enough for two bags,' I replied, replacing the tin.

'What about coupons?'

I checked the ration book.

'Yes, we're okay.'

'You'd better get two bags. Now come and sit down. There's something I want to tell you.'

I bit my fingernails. The kettle whistled.

'Just a minute.' I reached for the tea caddy, placed two spoonfuls in the pot and filled it with boiling water. After waiting for the tea to mash, I poured two cups, placed one on the edge of the table where Mum could reach it, and sat back in Dad's chair.

Ian finished his bottle and Mum burped him over her shoulder. She glanced down at the brooch. I looked away, sipped my tea and listened to Ian's hiccups.

* * * *

My mind wandered back to when Mum first took ill. She was five months pregnant at the time, and it was the start of the six-week school holidays.

Mum and Dad took me to a distant relative's farm in Lincolnshire, as I was recovering from bronchitis. Mum thought I would benefit from the fresh country air, which I did; plus the good wholesome food: fresh eggs, bacon, fruit picked from the orchard and home baked bread. No shop-bought produce in Auntie Edith's kitchen, no waste either. Everything went in the pig swill, even apple cores.

They had no children, so I had no one to play with, only my books and my rose-scented notelets. Uncle Wilf was a big man who smelt awful. He also had a massive chest and tummy, which he covered with a stained brown-checked shirt. Auntie Edith suggested I helped with the chores. Some I enjoyed, others were not so pleasant.

'Which is your favourite chicken?' Uncle Wilf asked one day, while I was scattering seeds in the yard.

'That one.' I pointed to a large brown hen pecking around my feet.

As soon as I spoke, he picked it up and wrung its neck. I screamed. I had never seen death before.

Uncle Wilf laughed at my tears.

4

'You'll not be crying tonight when you're eating it.' He walked away, chuckling. The chicken's head jerked beneath its body.

* * * *

Auntie Edith told me to help in the chicken shed, and tied a sack around my waist. The smell was terrible. It stuck in my throat like a lump of phlegm. I climbed the rickety wooden steps to get to the poor hens that lived in the top of the barn. With hardly any ventilation, my eyes began to smart, and I started to cough.

'You'll soon get used to it,' Uncle said. 'Clear them lungs out for you.'

Uncle Wilf called it a battery and told me a baker near Retford used the eggs his hens produced. The poor hens were housed on both sides in sloping wire mesh cages, three tiers high and stepped. The holes in the bottom of the cages were just wide enough to allow the eggs, when laid, to roll to the front and drop gently into a channel, ready for collection.

Beneath the rows of cages were rubberised continuous conveyor belts, power driven, four feet wide, which were static until they needed cleaning. With the power switched on, the belts moved along beneath the cages.

I stood on a wooden box at one end so I could reach, and scraped off all the muck with a broad-bladed knife. The droppings fell through a trapdoor in front of me, into a large container. My eyes and throat burned. I wanted to go home. By the time I'd finished, my arms, socks and sandals were filthy. Later, I enjoyed having a proper bath in a real bathroom, even though blisters covered my skin.

One day, Auntie Edith went into town on the bus and I was sitting in front of the dressing table in my bedroom writing letters to my friends. The room smelled of roses until Uncle Wilf came in. He sat near me, on the edge of the bed.

'That's a pretty dress you're wearing, Jacqueline,' he said, touching the hem.

'It's my summer sundress,' I replied, and looked down at the dress. It was a hand-me-down from my older cousin Brenda, but I didn't need to tell him that. I continued writing.

'Do you always wear plaits? I'd like to see your hair loose,' he said, then reached over and pulled away the slide that held the plaits on top of my head. My plaits fell down my back.

'There, that's better, you can remove the ribbons.' He nodded for me to do so.

'But I only undo them at night when I brush my hair before going to bed.'

'You can pretend, can't you?' He touched my ribbons.

I pulled away and moved his hand, then stared at him.

He placed his hands on the brass belt buckle hanging beneath his belly and went quiet for a moment.

'What are you learning at school?' he asked.

'Sums, poems, spelling, nature. I'm taking my scholarship next year. I'm going to be a doctor,' I replied, without looking at him.

'A doctor, eh?' He stroked his stained, whiskery chin. 'Do you play doctors and nurses with your friends?'

He came closer and stood behind me.

I looked at the hem of my dress and shuffled the chair further under the dressing table.

'I'm too old to play those games now.'

'So you're all grown up?' He placed his hands on my shoulders. 'Perhaps you'd like to dance.'

I eased myself away. I felt trapped.

'Come on, Jacqueline, show me how you dance.' He let go of my shoulders, pulled the chair back, took hold of my hands and pulled me towards him. 'Don't be shy – all young ladies like to dance, come on.' He rubbed his belt.

Reluctantly I stood up. It felt like my cheeks were glowing red. 'But I haven't had any lessons. My friend Susan goes to ballet and tap, and Catherine Clark, she has piano lessons –'

'Never mind them. I want to see what you can do. Come on, don't be shy.'

I didn't know where to look. I squeezed my hands together and looked down at my sandals.

A noise came from downstairs.

'Wilf, are you up there?'

It was Auntie Edith. She had come back from town.

'Coming, love, just getting changed,' he replied, and tiptoed out of my room and into his own.

Shaking, I sat at the dressing table, picked up my fountain pen and opened a new notelet.

Dear Mum, please....

* * * *

I shuddered as Mum spoke and took away the memories. Ian's hiccups had gone.

'Jacqueline, I'm talking to you. Are you listening?

'Sorry, Mum. What did you say?'

'Pass me my photo box out of the dresser, love, there's something I want to show you.'

I went over to the old sideboard and took out a biscuit tin with a picture of a thatched cottage on the lid. The first photograph I took out was a black and white picture of my sister Josie in her pram. Such a bonny baby; she'd weighed nine pounds at birth and Mum said she'd been an easier birth than either Ian or I, despite her size.

I looked at Josie's smiling face and thought back to a few months ago, when she hadn't been smiling. My mind drifted back again as I passed Mum the photographs and she began looking through the box.

* * * *

Mum's health deteriorated after she and Dad brought me home from the farm. Josie and I spent the second half of the summer holidays living with an aunt and uncle over at Mosborough, a tram and a long bus ride away. We shared a bedroom with their son Eric, who was the same age as me. He hated our being there and threw things at us at night when we went to bed.

'Stop it, Eric,' I shouted. 'We don't want to be here either.'

'You shouldn't have come then.' He threw his toy soldiers at us.

'I want my Mummy,' Josie cried, tears streaming down her face.

I couldn't answer. I was crying too. I held her close to me.

'When's Daddy coming for us, Jack-Jack?' Her arms wrapped tightly around my neck. Dad came over every Sunday and we cried when he left without us. He waved goodbye with the hanky he'd wiped his eyes with.

I answered her question. 'Soon, love, when Mummy's better.'

We cuddled up and cried together, with the sheet and blanket pulled over our heads. We didn't sleep though. It was too quiet. No drop-forge hammers thudding through the night. Strange unknown screeching noises scared us. The outside lavatory scared us too. It didn't have a water flush like ours at home. Uncle George called it an Earth Closet. It was across the yard, with a boxed-in raised wooden bench which had a round hole cut in it and a six foot drop below. Josie had to be lifted onto the seat.

'Hold me, Jack-Jack, don't let me fall.' Her arms clung to me while I held her.

The September school term started, and we were still at Mosborough. We were sent to local schools: Josie in the infants and me in the juniors. After a week, the teacher placed me in a class with the first year seniors. The other children didn't like us. We were from the city.

* * * *

'He's not your real dad, you know.'

Mum's words shocked me back to the present. 'What?'

'Your dad, he's not your real dad.'

I didn't know how to reply. Ian lay across her lap while she searched through the tin of photographs.

A sudden gust of wind came down the chimney, and a large belch of smoke tumbled into the room. I jumped up and took the baby from Mum. Holding him to my chest with one arm while wafting the smoke away with the other, I made my way to open the door. Mum followed me. We stood there for a few moments while the air cleared. Shivering, we closed the door and returned to the fireside. Another gust of wind blew, disturbing a patch of loose plaster on the ceiling, causing it to crash into the sink.

'I'll clean it up later,' I said as Ian cried. 'His nappy needs changing,' I sat back down.

'He's Josie's and Ian's dad, but not yours,' she said. 'But he loves you just as much.' She picked up the photographs that had fallen onto the floor.

Although I didn't want to hear, I had to know. I opened my knees as far as my skirt would allow, balanced Ian across my lap, and removed his soiled nappy.

'What do you mean he's not my real dad? We've all got the same name.' I thought for a minute. 'Joan Renshaw across the street, she's got a different dad and a different name to her brothers and sisters, and no one likes her because she's different.'

'That's because her new dad didn't adopt her. Your new dad, Charlie, adopted you when he married me, when you were four. She gave a faint smile and waited for a reply or some reaction.

I felt my cheeks flushing. *I'm adopted.* Her words slowly began to register. I continued to change Ian's nappy.

Mum didn't say any more. She passed me a clean muslin nappy and the jar of zinc and castor oil cream from the drawer beneath her chair. I took a clean piece of old nappy from the fireguard and dampened it in the pan of warm water on the hearth.

'Are you my real mum?' I asked, looking straight across at her.

'Of course I am, love.' Her blue eyes misted over and she reached out towards me.

I didn't respond to the gesture. 'Who is my dad then?' I asked, still concentrating on Ian's bottom, wiping it with the damp cloth and patting it dry.

Mum placed her hands back in her lap. 'Uncle Frank. Do you remember him? I have some photos of him somewhere.'

My face flushed again as my mind drifted back. 'You were married to Uncle Frank?'

'No, I…' She stopped, unsure what to say next.

'Why weren't you married to him? I didn't think you could have babies without being married.'

'Because… I couldn't,' she replied.

I smeared the thick white goo over Ian's reddened bottom. I didn't want to hear anymore. Ian began to cry.

'Shush, shush now, it'll soon be better.' I gently rocked him, then turned his small frame over onto the clean nappy and tickled his tummy, taking care where his tummy plug had been. His tiny arms jerked upwards, and he gave me a gurgling smile.

I took the pin off the front of my jumper and fastened the nappy, pulled down his vest, lifted him to my chest and cuddled him as tight as I dared.

I stood up, my heart filled with love, my eyes filled with tears, and the curdled milk spilled from his mouth.

'I'd better go and get Josie from school,' I said, cradling Ian in one arm and picking up the soiled nappy. I dropped it into the nappy pail under the sink where the slop bucket was kept. The gas burner for the wash tub, the washing board and scrubbing brushes, dirty clothes basket and sink plunger, were all hidden behind the green and white checked curtain fastened round the bottom of the sink. I wrapped a blanket around Ian and laid him in the pram by the doorway.

'Are you upset, love?' Mum asked, as I took my beret and coat from the back of the cellar door; my gloves fastened onto the cuffs with elastic.

'Well, it's not every day you find out you're adopted. Do they know at school?'

I didn't wait for an answer. I fastened my coat and looked into the pram. Ian was sound asleep.

'I'll not be long.' I stepped outside and closed the door behind me.

* * * *

My mind whirled with thoughts as I walked up our street, a row of grimy red-brick terraced houses, two up, two down and an attic. No one used their downstairs front rooms: no one could afford to heat them. There were four homes to each yard. Each yard had an entry in the middle, and all the houses had lavatories at the top of the yard and bathtubs hanging on the outside walls.

The bitter cold wind blew and I coughed. I tucked my hands into my gloves and pushed my long hair underneath the back of my coat collar. The Pikelet man was coming towards me.

'Pikelets, Oatcakes, Muffins,' he shouted, in a voice as harsh as the wind. His wicker basket was balanced on his head, with his produce laid on a clean white cloth. As he passed me, the smell of fresh teatime treats filled my nostrils. I hoped Mum would hear him and buy some.

The deafening sound of the steelworks' hammers faded as I neared the main road. I looked right and left and skipped across, and ran up the road by the side of the park. I could see a solitary dog walker through the railings, and an infant on the swing, his mother pushing it away from her, the child giggling as he came back towards her. I quickened my pace and hurried towards the school.

I stood with the mothers who were waiting for their offspring. Most of them had younger children with them, who were laughing, crying, screaming, or throwing toys from their prams.

I picked up the toys, gave them back to their owners and gave dirtied dummies to their mothers for them to lick clean and place back in the bawling infants' mouths. They thanked me and carried on chatting, their Coronation headscarves flapping in the wind, toddlers hanging onto their coat tails.

'How's your mum doing, Jacqueline, and that little brother of yours?' Mrs Brown from number twenty-three asked.

'They're getting better, thank you.' I replied.

She gave me a smile and patted my head as if I were a dog. I wondered if *she* knew of my adoption. I looked at the other women to see if they were looking at me any differently. The school bell rang, and shortly afterwards, boys and girls aged between five and seven came running towards the gates, clutching drawings. Coats were fastened askew, and hand-knitted balaclavas were plonked on heads. Shoes were unfastened, on the wrong feet, or on the wrong child.

As soon as I was in sight, Josie rushed towards me with opens arms, grabbed hold of my legs and gave me a hug.

'Jack-Jack!' She pushed the drawing into my hand. I bent down and gave her a hug, kissed her rosy-cheeked face and re-fastened her coat. I adjusted her bonnet, her wild unruly hair refusing to be contained.

'Jack-Jack, look,' she insisted.

She reminded me of myself when taking exams at school. I would rush home from school to show the results to Mum and wait anxiously to show Dad when he came in from work. The papers always said ten out of ten or nine out of ten, with a gold star to endorse it. Written in the teacher's script would be: "Jacqueline always works well, an excellent result," or "It's a pleasure to have Jacqueline in my class, she's so attentive."

I looked at Josie's picture. A drawing of a house stood towards the edge of the piece of paper, with matchstick people and a pram standing on green grass, a large white area behind them, and at the top of the page, a blue line for the sky. I wondered where these individual houses were. I had only ever seen them in rows, apart from in books, and the farm.

'That's very good,' I said. I rolled it up and put it in my pocket. 'Shall we do some more drawing when we get home?' I pushed Josie's small hands into her mittens and took hold of her so we could cross the road safely together.

'Ooh, yes,' she replied, swinging the hand holding mine to and fro. 'Will you draw a doggie for me to colour, please?' She looked up at me, her big blue eyes pleading.

'Of course I will.' I squeezed her hand. We skipped together down the lane, towards home.

Ian lay on his back, gurgling away when we arrived. Josie stood on tiptoe and peered into the pram.

'Baby Ian,' she cooed, and spun the row of yellow ducks strung across the front, startling him. His body jerked at the sudden movement. She kissed the cute baby picture painted on the front of her old high chair, biding its time between the pram and the sideboard until Ian was big enough occupy it.

Turning towards Mum, she ran the few steps and kissed her, then turned and looked at me.

'Picture, Jack-Jack, where's my picture?' She tugged at my skirt. I handed it to her as I hung up our coats.

'Mrs Brown asked after you,' I told Mum, as I closed the door and pushed the draught-stopper towards the gap.

Mum had folded the dried nappies and laid the table with an oilcloth cover for tea. The brooch and box of photographs had gone.

'Look, Mummy. It's our house and us.' Josie pushed the drawing at Mum, who took it from her and looked at the blue sky with the sun shining and the flowers in the garden.

'It's not exactly here, is it?' She looked at me and out of the grimy window at the smoke-filled sky. 'It's lovely, sweetheart,' she said, looking down at her bonny daughter. 'Let's pin it on the wall, so Daddy can see it when he comes home.'

I opened the sideboard drawer and handed Mum a small box of drawing pins. Removing two, she pressed them into the picture and through the layers of old wallpaper by the side of the kitchen cabinet.

'Jack-Jack's going to draw me a doggie,' Josie told Mum as she rummaged in the toy box beneath the large central table, with its three odd chairs and two stools.

I looked at the clock on the mantelshelf and quickly drew a

picture of a dog standing outside a kennel on the back of a piece of unused wallpaper. Josie, waiting with crayons in hand, positioned herself beneath the table.

Mum sat in her chair, darning Dad's socks, the sewing box by her side.

'I need to finish what I was telling you, love.'

'Not now, Mum. I've got to get the tea on.' I peeled some potatoes and carrots, chopped them into small pieces and added them to the pan of mutton stew that I had made yesterday. I had skimmed off the fat that had set on the top and placed it in a dish, which would do for Dad's packing up, with the meat I'd scraped off the bones.

I placed the pan on the stove and lit the gas. Dad would be here soon. My stomach lurched. Ian began to cry.

'It's coming,' I said, and took him from his pram, kissed his tears and handed him to Mum. She gently rocked and patted him while I made his bottle. As soon as the kettle whistled, I made a pot of tea, placed it on the table and covered it with a knitted cosy, and passed Ian's bottle to Mum, checked the fire and placed Dad's slippers in front of it.

The back door opened and smoke belched down the chimney again. The pegged rug in front of the fender lifted and the draught blew round our legs.

'Daddy, Daddy!' Josie ran to him, her chubby arms grabbing hold of his legs, as he drew the thick chenille curtain back over the door.

'I've drawn some pictures, Daddy.' She pushed the dog picture towards him. 'And this one,' she added, taking hold of his hand and pulling him towards the wall.

'Whoa, let me get in first, sweetheart,' he said, as he picked her up and kissed her on the cheek.

'Ugh, whiskers,' she giggled, and placed her arms around his neck.

I couldn't look, and turned back to the pan of stew. He bent over, kissed Mum, and looked at Ian, a beam of a smile spread across his face.

'How's he doing, and you?' He spoke quietly to Mum. She smiled and nodded.

'Are you okay, love?' He was talking to me. He removed his boots, coat, cap and muffler and hung them on the back of the cellar door, closed it and pushed the draught-stopper towards the gap at the bottom.

'These are nice and warm,' he said, as he pulled on his slippers and placed his empty snap box, an old Oxo tin, on the wooden draining board by the side of the sink.

'I said, are you okay, love?' He lifted the heavy pan off the stove and onto the table, and then ruffled the top of my hair.

I couldn't answer. Words were stuck in my throat. I wanted to run but I was trapped in the corner between the sink and the stove. I pushed him as I tried to pass.

'Hey,' he said. 'What's the matter?' He bent down, took hold of my arms and looked at me.

I burst into tears, and flung my arms around him. 'I love you, Dad,' I said and cried into his chest.

He held me tightly to him. 'Now, what's brought this on?' He stroked the back of my head for a minute and then still holding me, stood up and looked down at my face. 'And I love you too.'

2

I tossed and turned. The old army greatcoats thrown across the bed were too heavy for my skinny body. The warmed oven shelf had gone cold and I had cramp in both legs and feet. I climbed out and placed the cold shelf on the floor, straightened my nightie and waited for the cramps to cease. Drawing the curtains closer together did nothing to stop the ice forming on the inside of the windows. Shivering, I got back into bed and snuggled up to Josie, who was warm as toast.

I couldn't sleep. Mum's revelations had disturbed me. I remembered a time before Mum married, when Mum and I lived with Granddad and three of her sisters and their children. Their husbands had not yet come home from the war.

An image of a tall man in a khaki uniform came to me. I could see him now. His forage cap pulled low over his forehead; dark curly hair cut short; wrinkles at the side of his brown eyes. I remembered running to him as he came up the garden path. The tall man lifted me up, laughing and smiling. He whirled me round until I went dizzy, then carried me into the house, took off his cap and opened his kit bag.

'Close your eyes, and no peeking,' he said.

I could hear paper rustling and couldn't wait to open my eyes.

'You can open them NOW!' He bent down and held out a golden -furred teddy bear with a blue ribbon around its neck. 'It's for you, Jacqueline.'

I reached out to touch its soft, furry body. I looked at him and then up at Mum. She was smiling, but there were tears in her eyes.

Instead of her usual pinny, she was wearing a pretty dress, beads around her neck, and lipstick. I jumped up and down and took the teddy from him.

'Don't I get a kiss and a hug, then?' he said.

Holding the teddy in one arm, I reached out to him with the other. He picked me up and hugged the teddy and me.

I kissed his cheek, which was rough, and struggled for him to put me down; I wanted to play with the teddy bear.

He took Mum into his arms, kissed her for a long time, and stroked her back, and then they both looked down at me and back at each other. I ran off to show my cousins what Uncle Frank had brought me.

* * * *

The wetness seeped through my nightie and onto my skin. I jumped out of bed, felt my way to the light switch by the doorway, and turned it on.

'Josie, wake up,' I said. 'You've wet the bed.'

She sat up, rubbing her eyes and started crying.

'Come here, love,' I said, and gave her a cuddle. 'Let's get you out of that wet nightie.' I went over to the chest of drawers and took out a clean one. 'Arms up,' I said, as she lifted her arms up in the air. 'Ugh, Stinky pee,' Pulling a face, I pulled the wet nightie over her head.

'Tinky pee, tinky pee,' she giggled, while I placed the clean one over her plump little body. She shivered with the coldness of it, and tried to climb back into bed.

'Not yet,' I said, and wrapped my cardigan round her shoulders.

I dragged the heavy coats and wet sheet off the bed, and wiped the brown rubber mattress-cover with the soiled sheet.

'Wait there.' I said, as she tried climbing back into bed again. Her teeth were chattering. Taking a clean flannelette sheet from the blanket chest, I remade the bed.

'Have we to say our prayers again?' she asked.

'No, once a night is enough.' We climbed into bed, and cuddled together, her arms around my neck. I jumped back out; I'd forgotten to turn off the light.

'Tell me a story, Jack-Jack.'

* * * *

It was six o'clock when I awoke and heard Dad going downstairs. Slipping my arms into my cardigan over the top of my nightie, I picked up the oven shelf and the wet sheet and followed him down.

He began raking the ashes out of the grate.

'Here, Dad, I'll do that if you want to make a pot of tea.' I put the sheet under the sink and the shelf back in the oven. Still dark outside, I left the curtains closed.

The steelworks next door changed shifts and the hammers started again: thump, thump, thump. The windows and floor vibrated, along with the cups and bottles in the cabinet. I looked up at the ceiling. The last hole was no larger and there were only flakes of plaster in the sink.

Dad raked out a shovel full of ashes and placed them in an old bucket we kept outside for spreading over the ice. He came back in coughing and put the kettle on, then washed himself under the tap by the sink.

I went down into the cellar. There were no sticks chopped. Finding a block of wood, I placed it on the bottom step. It toppled over. Replacing it, I stood on two of the bricks and picked up the axe. My wrist twisted with its weight as I brought it down on the block of wood. The piece of wood shot off to one side. I re-positioned the block, holding it in place with my other hand, and raised the axe again.

'Jack, your mother's calling for you,' Dad shouted.

* * * *

Ian's cries filled my ears as I climbed the steps. I placed the shovel full of coal and sticks in the hearth and made Ian's bottle. Dad took it upstairs to Mum while I pushed some screwed-up newspaper into the grate, arranged the sticks on top and added a few pieces of coal. It wouldn't take long to get going with the grate still warm.

Standing the shovel on the bottom bar, I reached up to the mantelshelf for the matches and lit the paper. Then, holding a large sheet of newspaper across the shovel, I let the draught draw the fire. It was trying to draw my nightie too, so I tucked it between my knees. The sheet of paper soon scorched and caught alight. I pushed it into the fire and held it down with the poker until it burned away. Then I got dressed.

Dad sat by the fire, warming his hands and drinking his tea. I cut him two slices of bread off the loaf and tried to spread it with margarine, but it was too cold and solid, so I grated some with the cheese grater, sprinkled it on the bread, and handed it to him.

'The fire's going nicely now, love,' he said, and threw on the rest of the coal. He sat quietly drinking his tea while I sat at the table and drank mine.

'I see Mum told you, then.' He waved his hand for me to come over to him.

I went over to him and sat on his knee. He was wearing his work clothes, which smelled of iron and steel oil. He cuddled me to him. I could hear his chest wheezing.

'Mum's not going to die, is she?' I asked, wrapping my arms around him.

'Of course not. She just thought it was time you knew a few things about yourself before you found out from someone else. She'll tell you more when she's good and ready.

'It doesn't matter that you're not my real dad, does it?' I held him tight and stared into the flames.

He gave me a squeeze. 'Not at all. I love you just as much as Josie and Ian. You're a good girl, Jack — you've been a godsend to your mother. Now then, did you do me any packing up?'

I kissed his cheek, and stroked the top of his bald head.

Coldness rushed into the room as I opened the cellar door and shut it quickly. I grabbed his outdoor clothes and placed them over the fireguard to warm. He finished his tea, and went up the yard to the lav.

'Right, love, I'll see you at tea-time,' he said when he returned, and adjusted his belt and braces. He put on his boots, coat, tucked his muffler around his neck and pulled on his cap. I handed him the Oxo tin.

'Look after your mother,' he said, as he felt in his pocket for his tram fare, then kissed my cheek and went out into the smog-filled air.

* * * *

I ate a slice of bread and margarine and drank another cup of tea as I watched the draught move the thick net curtain at the window, and then I emptied the slops and mousetraps before resetting them. I chopped more sticks and put more coal on the fire before calling Josie up for school. She came down, rubbing her eyes, and made her way to the sink. I washed her face and hands, then brushed her thick, wiry hair. It didn't grow downwards but up. She screamed as I teased out the painful lugs. When she started scratching her head, I knew I'd have the horrible task of combing it through with the nit comb after Friday night's bath. Her clothes were warming on the fireguard and she managed to dress herself.

'Too tight,' she said, pulling on her garters below her knees.

I tucked my finger between the sock and the elastic.

'Okay, I'll make you some more,' I took the sewing box from the sideboard cupboard and looked for some elastic, but there was only a small piece left.

'Here, have mine,' I said, and slid the pieces of elastic down over my grey knee-high socks. 'They might need adjusting.'

I cut a slice of bread off the loaf.

'Look, Jack-Jack, they're holding up.' She stood in front of me, shaking each leg in turn. I couldn't believe that my garters actually fitted her.

'Come on now, get your breakfast or you'll be late.' I spread the slice of bread with margarine.

'Can I have some sugar on please, Jack-Jack?' She looked at me from across the table, her big blue eyes pleading.

'There's none left,' I said, showing her the empty blue bag.

Her face dropped, she scowled, and then smiled as I took another packet out of the cabinet and sprinkled the bread with sugar. Her eyes lit up and she held out her hand. I poured her some tea and added condensed milk.

'Come on,' I said when she had finished and climbed off the stool. 'Let's have you up the yard to the lav.'

* * * *

'Bye baby bunting…' she began singing as she went upstairs to see Mum and Ian after I'd washed her hands.

'Come on, dozy Josie,' I shouted after a few minutes. 'You'll be late.' She came to the top of the stairs and holding onto the banister, took a few steps towards me and then jumped the last three steps. 'You'll be doing that once too often, young lady,' I said, and caught her in my arms. 'I'll not always catch you. One day I'll walk away just as you jump.'

She held her arms out for her coat, then giggled and started turning around in circles.

'Stop it,' I said, wrapping the coat over her head.

'Is there anything you want, Mum, before I go?' I shouted upstairs.

'No love, I'll be okay.'

'Don't try getting up till I'm back, will you?' I managed to get Josie's arms in her coat and fastened it, along with her bonnet and shoes.

'Where's your dinner money?'

She shook her mitten; the coins rattled inside. I checked the fire and the guard, before leaving the house with one sock around my ankle, the other round my calf.

* * * *

'It's only me, I'll be up in a minute,' I shouted upstairs when I returned and rubbed some Glymiel Jelly into my hands and cracked ankles. My chilblains were stinging.

I put the kettle on, made some tea and took a cup up to Mum, who was sitting in bed with a woollen bed-jacket fastened around her shoulders, nursing Ian.

'I'll get up now you're back,' she said as she drank her tea.

'Do you want me to carry Ian down?'

She gave a weak smile. 'Please, love,' she replied.

I placed her clothes over my arm and took Ian from her. Downstairs, I placed Ian in his pram and put her clothes over the fireguard to warm. I noticed her knickers were stained. I put them in the nappy pail, went back upstairs and took a clean pair out of her drawer.

Mum followed me down and dressed in front of the fire. I helped her with her stockings and slippers and then she flopped into her chair.

'Do you want anything to eat yet?' I asked.

'No, love, just another cup of tea will do. About yesterday…'

My stomach did a quick somersault. Half of me wanted to know the truth and the other half didn't. I moved towards the sink.

'Not now, Mum, the dishes need washing.'

She took hold of my hand as I passed.

'Sit down, Jacqueline.' I felt myself blushing.

'Here, I want you to have this.' She held the brooch in her hand again, and then pressed it into mine. 'Your father gave me this. He said my auburn hair would set it off beautifully, and it did. I want you to keep it.'

22

'It's yours, Mum. Why would I want it?' I tried to give it back.

'Because one day you will understand, so for now, just put it away in your drawer and forget about it. Here, you might as well take these as well.'

She handed over two photographs of Uncle Frank, but not as I remembered him. He wasn't wearing a uniform: he wore a shirt and a sleeveless jumper, and had a mop of curly black hair; he looked so familiar.

'You're his double,' she said. 'You've got his good looks too.'

I stood up, went over to the sideboard and looked in the mirror. She was right – I did look like him. Not at all like Mum, with fair skin and freckles, blue eyes and auburn hair. I had a much darker skin tone, with grey-green eyes and dark brown hair. I stared at my reflection and the photograph. I turned and went back to her.

'But they're your photos, Mum, you should keep them.'

'No love, I've got Charlie now. He's a good man and between us we've got Josie and Ian, and you of course.' She gave me a hug. 'The best gift of all.'

A couple of shadows passed the window, followed by a knock on the door. I went to answer it.

'Who is it?' Mum asked.

3

'It's the midwife and the school board bobby,' I replied, after opening the door.

'I can see you're going to be busy for a while. I'll come back later,' said the man from school as he wrote in his notebook. I took the milk from the windowsill and put it in the pantry.

'Hello, Jacqueline, how are things?' the midwife asked as she came in the house and removed her coat, scarf and gloves, and then re-pinned her hat firmly back in place. She lifted her large black bag on to the table and took out some papers.

'I'll put the kettle on, do you want a cup?' I asked, as she came over to where Mum sat.

'I wouldn't mind, Jacqueline. It's bitter cold out there today.' She reached her hands over the fireguard. 'How do you cope with the noise of those hammers all day and night? It would drive me mad.' She rubbed her hands in front of the flames, then turned around and warmed her back.

'You get used to it,' Mum replied, moving the washing on the fireguard to one side.

'Have you attended any more births since I last saw you?' The Midwife looked at me with a grin on her face – she was the same midwife who had delivered Mum's sister Edna's baby, earlier this year.

* * * *

Auntie Edna and her husband didn't want to have the baby in the flat where they lived, so she came to Mum and had the baby in Mum and Dad's bed. She arrived early one Sunday morning in May, in a lot of pain.

I was told to make a fire in the front bedroom, and then go and fetch Auntie Doris. With a shovel full of hot coals from the kitchen fire, I took them upstairs and placed them in the fire grate, then added a few sticks and some coal. The fire was blazing in no time. Mum settled Auntie Edna into bed, while I went to fetch Auntie Doris.

'She's about a week early,' she said, flipping her cigarette and pulling off her pinny. 'I'll just get my bag and then we'll be off, Jacqueline.' Auntie Doris always pronounced my name as Jack-a-lene. No one else did, only Auntie Doris.

We called at the midwife's house on the way back. Her husband said she was out on an emergency, and he would give her the message when she returned.

* * * *

Auntie Edna's husband Les paced the floor in the kitchen, asking if everything was all right every time I came back down from the bedroom. I was busy making tea for everyone, and boiling pans of water.

'You'd better boil the bacon scissors up for ten minutes, Jacqueline,' called Mum. 'I don't think she's going to last till the midwife arrives.'

I made sure the doors were shut tight so Uncle Les couldn't hear if Auntie Edna screamed. Mum said she had known men pass out if they were within earshot of their wife's labour pains. I checked in the cupboard to make sure we had some smelling salts, just in case.

'Jacqueline,' Auntie Doris shouted down. 'Get the scissors and some more towels, love.'

I poured the boiling water into an empty pan and tipped the

scissors into a clean towel, with Uncle Les watching my every move.

'No point in hanging around here just now, Les,' Dad said. 'Might as well take a walk in the park.'

'Can I come too?' Josie asked.

* * * *

'Come on Edna, push.'

Mum and Auntie Doris were holding onto her and urging her to push. She was crying and screaming. I put the wrapped scissors on the blanket chest and the towels over the bed rail.

'I can't,' Auntie Edna screamed. 'It's the ridge on the oven shelf – it's pressing into my back.

Mum and Auntie Doris tried to move it to make her more comfortable. Edna winced as she pressed her body down onto the towel-wrapped cast-iron shelf.

'Move it, Doris, I can't stand it,' she moaned.

'Edna, you've got to have it, the bed-springs have gone.'

'Good Lord, when will this end?' she cried again.

I stood by the bottom of the bed, peering between the rails, watching. Auntie Edna suddenly gave a loud gasp. I heard a squelching noise, and saw a bloody mass appear between her legs. My eyes widened.

'Steady now, Edna, here it comes,' said Mum, who was now blocking my view. Auntie Edna gave a scream that was more like a wolf howl. I dashed to the bedroom door and onto the landing. *She's dying, and she's bleeding to death.*

I heard a knock and the back door opening. I ran downstairs: the midwife. I pulled her to the bottom of the stairs.

'Quick. Up here. She's bleeding to death.' I ran back upstairs; the midwife followed. When I got to the top, I stepped back to allow her to pass.

'Jacqueline, are you there? Go and make some tea, love,' Auntie Doris called.

26

Glad to be out of the bedroom, I stopped halfway down the staircase. I remembered Mum saying previously that there would be a lot of blood. Mum and Auntie Doris didn't seem bothered and the midwife was here now, so it must be all right.

I took the tray of tea upstairs, and then nearly dropped it as I entered the bedroom. Something bloody was burning on the fire. My bottom lip and chin quivered.

'Is it dead?' I looked at them and put the tray on the blanket chest, and then ran to Mum.

'Of course it's not dead,' said Mum, giving me a hug, 'She's there – look.'

Auntie Edna looked pale and tired. She smiled as she held the baby to her chest.

'It's a girl,' said Mum.

'But what's that burning in the fire?' I asked.

'That's the afterbirth. The midwife's checked it and it's no good anymore.'

'When I saw all that blood, I thought it was the baby.' I started laughing and crying at the same time.

The midwife looked over at Mum and Auntie Doris. They both gave me a hug.

'You'll have to get used to that, Jacqueline, if you want to be a doctor,' Auntie Doris laughed.

* * * *

The midwife's voice brought my thoughts back to the present baby, my lovely brother.

'Have you had any problems, Margaret?' she asked.

Mum smiled. 'No, he's a good baby, considering what he's been through.'

'How is he getting on with the special formula?' She held the cup in both hands while talking to Mum and drinking the tea. 'It'll be a while before he can go on to Ostermilk, Margaret. He'll need more weight on him first. I'll have a look at him.' She handed me the cup. 'Thanks, Jacqueline, just what I needed.' She placed a clean blanket on the table.

Ian started crying as Mum handed him over.

'Oh, diddums, diddums,' said the midwife as she removed his shawl and placed him on the blanket. His little fists and legs kicked, and he bawled, tears running down the sides of his face and into his ears. I didn't think such tiny lungs could power so much noise.

'Has he been to the clinic for weighing, Margaret?'

'Yes, Jacqueline's taken him.' They both looked at me and smiled.

'He now weighs six and a quarter pounds,' I said, proudly.

She looked at her papers. 'Ah, yes, I have it here.' She read the card. 'He is doing well, keep up the good work.' She examined his body and studied the pink and blue marbling on his legs, which she gently pressed.

They reminded me of Auntie Doris's mottled legs, which were dark red and brown. She got hers from standing in front of the fire too long. She would stand with her back to the fire and lift up the back of her dress and pinny.

'Just warming my brains,' she would say. Sometimes she would say something cheeky like, 'Just warming our Des's supper up.' When she said this, she would be facing the fire while lifting her dress and pinny. The grown-ups would laugh, but my cousins and I just looked at each other.

The midwife wrapped Ian back in his shawl, passed him to me and looked at Mum.

'What about you, Margaret?'

'I'm okay, love,' Mum replied.

'Has your milk dried up yet?'

'Yes, just about.' She unbuttoned her cardigan.

'I'll just have a look, and a little feel if that's okay, Margaret. My hands are still warm.'

She smiled as Mum slipped her brassiere and underskirt straps down over her arms.

'Yes, everything seems okay there,' the midwife said as she looked and felt Mum's breasts.

'What about down below?'

'Everything's okay,' Mum lied. I remembered the stained knickers.

The midwife sat in Dad's chair and wrote up her notes. 'You're getting the welfare orange juice and cod liver oil, aren't you?'

'Yes, Jacqueline fetches it for us, although they won't take the oil. Josie makes out she's going to vomit, and that's coming from someone who can eat anything! Mind you, I can't blame them. Have you ever tasted it?'

'I have, and can see why they don't like it.'

She put her papers back in the large bag and went over to the pram handle where her coat hung.

'Everything's okay, Margaret – there's no need for me to come again. Just continue with the welfare clinic. They'll need you to visit the clinic when you're able.' She pulled on her coat and gloves and opened the door. 'It's getting worse out there. Freezing smog coming in now.' She wrapped her scarf around her nose and mouth, shook her head and looked up at the steelworks chimneys, spilling out their smoke and soot.

'Thanks for everything, Gill,' Mum called.

'Thanks for the tea, Jacqueline. Cheerio, Margaret.' She picked up her bag and fastened it on the back of the pushbike. 'Morning Doris,' she said, nearly bumping into Auntie Doris as she came around the corner from the entry.

* * * *

Auntie Doris. Her long tweed coat tightly fastened with a matching tie belt, a Coronation headscarf fastened around her head and tied under her chin, with a few orange curls poking out on her forehead. Hands stuffed in her coat pockets with a shopping bag hanging from one arm.

'Morning Jacqueline,' she said, as she walked straight into the kitchen, cigarette hanging off her bottom lip. 'Have you got that kettle on?'

She removed her headscarf. A mass of bright orange frizz fell around her reddened face. Taking another few drags on the cigarette, she took it from her mouth, flipped the burning end off into the fire and tucked it behind her ear.

'What have you done to your hair, Doris?' Mum asked, frowning at the brightness. 'You'll have it falling out one of these days with all the different dyes you put on it.'

'I thought it would get me noticed,' she replied, laughing and coughing at the same time.

Get her noticed! You could see her coming a mile off. If she stood still long enough, you'd think it was a Belisha beacon. No wonder she covered it up with a headscarf.

'Look at you then,' she said, peering beneath the blanket wrapped around Ian. 'Isn't he coming on a treat?' She took him from Mum and looked him over.

'Has that kettle boiled yet?' she shouted over to me, laughing because I'd only just put it on.

'Not be a minute,' I replied. I stood in the corner waiting for it to boil, nibbling my nails.

'Are you okay, Margaret? What did the midwife have to say?' She passed Ian back to Mum while she removed her coat, and then stood warming her "brains" in front of the fire.

'What's up then, run out of coal?' she said. She stuffed the poker into the fire, looked over at me and grinned, then sat in Dad's chair and lit her tab-end. She coughed and brought up a load of phlegm and spat it in the fire.

'Is that why you wanted more coal on – to get rid of that lot?' I asked.

'You cheeky bugger.' Her laugh soon turned into a hacking cough.

I gave her a cup of tea, then went down the cellar for some more coal.

'That's better,' she said, as I tipped it into the fire. She pulled me towards her and turned me round, stroking my hair.

'Look at your hair. Come here, where's your brush?'

I moved toward the sideboard drawer to get the hairbrush.

'Are your ribbons in there?' she asked.

'I think so. They'll be creased if they are.' I pulled out a couple of red gingham ribbons and the hairbrush and took them over. She looked at the tattered ribbons.

'They won't do.' She took the iron from the cupboard by the fireplace, and placed a thick blanket on the kitchen table. Everything took place here: ironing, baking, wallpaper pasting, bandaging torn knees and nit combing.

Auntie Doris climbed up on the chair and onto the table and looked up at the single light bulb in a double socket, swinging from a single cord in the ceiling. The ceiling laths showed beneath the fallen plaster.

'You want to get onto that landlord o' yours, Margaret,' she said. 'He gets away with murder. Cheeky bugger charges you seven and six a week and he can't be bothered to do the repairs.'

She plugged the iron's flex into the socket. There was a loud bang and the light went out.

'It must have fused,' I said. I lit a taper in the fire and went to the pantry at the top of the cellar steps to turn off the mains switch. There were four fuses. I pulled them out in turn and checked the wires. The third fuse wire had snapped. The replacement wires were on top of the fuse box. I doused the taper and went over to the kitchen window. 'There's only ten amp wire left, all the five amp's has gone,' I said.

'Put ten in,' Auntie Doris said, as she lit a cigarette. 'It'll be alright.'

'But it's the five amp's that's fused.'

'It'll do till you get some. You're not going to trail right down to Hillsborough, are you, just for some bloody fuse wire?' Smoke poured out of her nose and mouth as she spoke.

I wasn't sure. I looked at Mum.

Mum nodded. 'We'll get some when we go shopping, love. You

can change it back then if you want.'

'Will Dad know when he comes home?' I asked, still concerned.

'I doubt it, love. It were gaslights when we came to live here.' Mum and Auntie Doris laughed.

I replaced the fuse wire and switched the power back on. There was another loud bang. I jumped and turned around. Auntie Doris stood behind me laughing. She had two saucepan lids in her hands and she banged them together. It made the same sound.

'You rotten pig,' I said, and rushed at her. 'That wasn't funny.'

She backed off, laughing and coughing at the same time.

'Oh Jacqueline,' she said, tears streaming down her cheeks. 'You should have seen your face, when you turned roun'…'

She couldn't speak for laughter, going blue in the face.

'Serves you right, the shock could have killed me.'

She burst out laughing again. 'The shock could have …'

'Come on, let's do your hair,' she said, when she'd finally calmed down. She was still chuckling while ironing the ribbons, before she climbed up on the table again to pull out the plug.

Sitting in Dad's chair, she turned me round with my back towards her and began brushing my hair.

A thought crossed my mind.

'Mum, did Gill the midwife deliver me and Josie?' Auntie Doris reached around and pulled my hand away from my mouth. Looking at my fingernails, she tapped them with the brush.

'I delivered you,' she said.

I looked across at Mum, who nodded.

'Wasn't Gill there then?'

'We didn't have midwives when you were born,' Mum said.

'Your Mum delivered most of them on the Sutton estate, with her having nursing experience.' Auntie Doris added. 'She told me what I had to do when you were due and that was it. I gave you your name and the scar on your head.'

'What scar on my head?'

She felt around on the top of my head. 'This one, feel here.' She raised my hand up to my head. 'Feel that?'

I felt around with my fingers until I found a tiny hollow. I'd never noticed it before. 'Is that it?' I said.

Auntie Doris looked at the place where I was poking my scalp.

'Here, look with this.' She reached into her handbag, pulled out her gilt compact and opened it. She blew the face powder off the mirror and tilted it towards the top side of my head.

My finger was still tracing the hollow. She moved my hair to one side.

'There – can you see it?'

I looked in the small mirror and saw a small bald crescent shape, no bigger than the tip of a nail file. 'Is that it?' I put my finger in the hollow. 'How did it happen?'

'It was my middle fingernail. I did it when I was pulling you out.' She released my hair and carried on brushing it.

I looked across at Mum, not knowing whether to believe her or not. Mum nodded in confirmation.

'Yes, it's true, love. And she gave you your name. I wanted to call you Wendy, but Doris wanted Jacqueline. As she'd delivered you, I thought it befitting.' They looked at each other and smiled.

She continued brushing my hair until it shone, and then plaited it into two long braids. They hung down my back like braided horse's tails. She added the ribbons and fastened them in two large bows.

'There, you look like you belong to someone now, instead of Orphan Annie.'

I looked in the mirror. My hair did look nice. I wondered why I'd never noticed the tiny scar before.

'I'll go and change the beds. Then we can wash the sheets,' I said, and left her and Mum talking.

I looked again in the upstairs mirror as I changed the bedding and checked in the wardrobes for any other clothes that needed washing.

My long white bridesmaid dress with pink bows had fallen off its hanger. I had worn it for Uncle Eric and Auntie Joy's wedding four years ago. Every girl dreamed of being a bridesmaid. I was so lucky they picked me out of all my cousins. They had chosen one child from either side of the family. Auntie Joy had chosen her sister's daughter, Irene. At seven, she was a year older than me and twice as big. I looked at the pink satin bows around the bottom frill, and the large-brimmed bonnet with pink bow – now squashed flat, and the heart-shaped muff. I remembered the white sandals, which were used afterwards for the May Day parade and the Whitsuntide Walk.

The wedding eve had been so exciting. Irene and I had slept at Auntie Joy's parent's house in their spare bedroom. We sat at the kitchen table, having supper: a biscuit and a drink of Ovaltine while Auntie Joy wound rags into our hair to make ringlets. Mine had been put in too tight and I couldn't sleep. Next morning, red marks appeared along the back of my neck and scalp, but they were soon forgotten, as the rags were removed and long bouncy ringlets danced over my shoulders and we were dressed in our bridesmaids' outfits.

I hung up the dress and tried to straighten the bonnet, collected the bedding and went downstairs.

'Come on then, Jacqueline, let's get stuck into the washing,' Auntie Doris said, throwing her tab end into the fire.

She pulled an Empire apron over her head and fastened it behind her back, then turned her headscarf the other way up, trapping the mass of orange curls inside it and rolling the corner over the top-knot and tucking it underneath like a turban. She moved the vase of plastic anemones Mum had once bought at a jumble sale and placed them on the sideboard. The green and white chequered cloth that covered the washtub was removed and she climbed onto the wooden board and opened the window. The cold wind howled through, along with the louder thud of the hammers. We waited a while, and looked up at the ceiling to see if any more plaster was likely to fall before removing the board. She pulled the heavy tub away from the wall and set Ian's bath behind to catch the washing.

I passed her the gas ring that was attached to the gas pipe by a rubber tube. She lit it and shoved it under the tub. I passed her the rubbing board from under the sink and the orangey red soap, followed by a bucket of water, which she emptied into the tub.

'Water's slow this morning Jacqueline,' she said, as she attached the mangle to the top of the tub.

I passed her more buckets of water. Mum had taken the clean laundry upstairs to put away, and Ian was asleep in his pram.

'Do you remember Uncle Frank, Auntie Doris?' I asked.

'Course I do, good lookin' fella. If your mother hadn't got him, I would.'

When the tub was full, she plunged her red hands and arms in amongst the clothes.

'He thought a lot about your Mum, and you. Never came empty handed either. Always brought something for the kids and food for the table. Oh no, listen to that lot.' She nodded her head towards the window. The smog had lifted and the rain lashed down, beating on the panes.

Auntie Doris had three children. Her husband never came back from the war. She had a new man in her life now, Des. She never said much about him, and Mum and Auntie Mary gave him strange looks when they saw him.

She rubbed soap onto the clothes, rubbed them against the board, dipped them back in the tub and then squeezed the water out by putting them through the mangle. The sheets were next, then the towels. She used the dolly posh for these, shoving and mixing the larger items in the water while I pushed them through the mangle and dropped them in the bath for rinsing. A patch of soapsuds stuck to the front of Auntie Doris's turban.

'Why didn't she marry him?' I asked, as I rested my arms from turning the mangle.

'He were already married,' she said, and wiped her forearm across her forehead. 'I think we'll have your Dad's work clothes in next. Jacqueline, Jack-a-lene…are you listening? Your Dad's work clothes.' She turned to look at me.

'What's the matter?' asked Mum, who had come downstairs, an anxious look on her face.

I stared at her and wiped my hands on my pinny.

I finally found my voice. 'Where's is he now, then?' I looked at Auntie Doris and then Mum, who had obviously heard some of the conversation.

They both spoke together,

'He's dead,' said Auntie Doris.

'I told him he couldn't –' Mum's words tapered off as they looked at each other through the steam. Neither spoke.

'How many more lies am I going to be told?' I screamed at them, and pulled off my pinny. 'Lies, liars, the lot of you.'

I pushed past Auntie Doris and ran to the door. 'I hate you, I hate you,' I shouted, as I ran up the yard to the lav and sat on the seat, crying.

4

I don't know how long I'd been in there when there was a knock at the lav door. I was wet, and freezing cold.

'Come on, Jacqueline – you can't stop in there, you'll catch your death. Come and have a cup of tea. The washing's done and I've just mashed.' Auntie Doris's voice came through the door.

'Go away. I don't want to talk to you.'

'Well I need to use the lav, so can you move to one side?' I gave half a laugh and half a cry, and stood to one side.

'You know there's no lock on the door,' I shouted.

The door opened and she came inside. I could smell the carbolic soap, bleach, and soda as she raised her apron and skirt, and pulled down her knickers.

'Come on, love, don't go upsetting your mum any more,' she said, as she sat on the seat. 'She's only doing what she thinks is right.'

I slouched, shivering, one knee bent and my foot pressed against the wall as she spoke.

'Well, is he dead or isn't he?' I continued, looking down at the floor, at the rain running in beneath the door.

'He is now, but he wasn't when your Mum married your Dad, Charlie. Your Mum told him that when she married – he had to break all contact. It wouldn't have been fair on Charlie as he was adopting you. It was a hard thing for your Mum to do at the time. She still had feelings for him. But then he died a couple of years ago. I saw it in the newspaper and told your Mum.'

She got up from the bench, pulled up her knickers, and smoothed her skirt and pinny down.

'Don't be hard on her, love. She's been through a lot. Come on, let's get that cup of tea before it goes cold.' She pulled me towards her and gave me a hug.

'God's truth, lass, you're all skin and bone, I've seen more fat on a chip. Let's get you inside and warmed up.' She knocked the whitewash off the back of my jumper as we ran down the path.

'He wasn't a real uncle, was he?'

The lines of wet washing hung from wall to wall. The window was still open and the steam rose and fell. I couldn't see her face because of the hanging sheets. Her red hands were visible as she poured tea into the spotted cups. Auntie Doris pushed me towards the fire. I began to cough, and sat in Dad's chair, trying to get warm. Auntie Doris went into the cellar and came back with a shovelful of coal, flung it on the fire and slipped her coat around my shoulders. Mum passed me a cup of tea and stroked my head as she pulled me towards her. I put the cup in the hearth and held her hand over mine.

* * * *

About a week later, both Dad and I came down with chest infections. Auntie Doris came more often as Mum was still too weak, and Dad and I were in bed, unable to help. By the weekend, we were no better, despite Mum and Auntie Doris covering our chests with hot kaolin poultices, mine held in place by a crepe bandage and a tight liberty bodice. They decided we needed a home visit from the doctor. The surgery was about three miles away from where we lived, so Auntie Doris walked to tell him. He came later that day, and after examining us, said we both had bronchitis. He prescribed medicine and said he would call back in a couple of days. We were to stay in our beds for at least another week. Mum and Dad were worried. Dad couldn't afford time off work.

After three days, I managed to get up, and Dad went back to work the following Monday, even though he was still poorly.

Auntie Doris did the washing by herself that day, and I did the ironing a few days later when it was dry.

* * * *

It was Friday evening when the rent man called.

'Hello Mr Simpson,' I said, as I opened the door. 'Mum says will it be alright if she misses this week, as Dad's been off work with his chest? He's gone back now though.'

Mr Simpson looked though his book. 'Yes, I think that will be all right.' He scanned the past few weeks, to see if we had missed any previous payments.

'Mind it's only one week though,' he said, as he made a note in his book and bid good night.

I also asked the same favour of the "Death Hunter", as Dad called him – the man from the Prudential, and the "Perm any eight from ten" man, who collected the football pools money.

'We'll have to share it fifty-fifty if he wins, tell him,' he laughed, and walked away whistling.

Mum's health improved every day, and Ian grew and began to recognise faces.

I loved it when he recognised me. He loved me to bathe him, and I enjoyed it too, holding his back and head, flicking the warm water up onto his chest, and gently washing the soft, fluffy tufts of hair on his head. Then he'd give thanks by squirting a wee-wee at me. I couldn't wait for him to get older so I could take him to the football matches.

We lived near Sheffield Wednesday's football ground, and every Saturday afternoon after half time, the gates opened and kids could go in for free. We couldn't see anything, as there were thousands of men on the Spion Kop. We'd tap someone in the back of a leg.

'Please mister, can we get past?' That's all we had to say to any of the men standing at the back. They would look down and see us, then lift us up over their heads and pass us man to man, all the way to the front. Just like flying, we were on the front wall in no time. The problem with being at the front was that we would be last out, and we'd miss getting the rosettes if there was a cup-tie. The kids outside the ground would be waiting for the final whistle and as soon as the crowds started coming out, they would ask for their rosettes.

We used to have competitions to see who could collect the most.

* * * *

I also loved playing school with Josie; she was so keen to learn. Every evening after tea, she took out her blackboard and easel. Dad told us he'd had to use a slate when he went to school. I chalked some sums on the board and she copied them into her book to work out.

Before Josie had even started school, she'd helped the gas man when he came to empty the meter. He would go down into the cellar and empty the coins into a metal canister, come back up, empty it out on to the kitchen table and count the pennies into stacks of twelve. Josie would watch and count along with him. He wrapped each shilling pile into a roll of stiff brown paper, like the stuff sugar came in, and put them into his satchel. There were always a few coins that didn't make a full shilling, so he would slide them across to Mum, and depending how many there were, she would give us one each and put the rest in her purse.

Josie learned the alphabet and was spelling words in no time, and I was forever drawing pictures for her to colour. I vowed that when I became a doctor, I would buy her a ready printed book to colour.

* * * *

With Mum now well on the mend, and Dad much better, although he still coughed and wheezed a lot, I would soon be going back to school.

As it was Friday; I went to where Dad worked to get his wages at twelve o'clock, and took them straight back to Mum, who opened the packet and began distributing amounts into various tins. She put some money in her purse and gave it to me with her shopping book, for me to get the weekly food shopping in.

'Will you get me some sanitary towels from the chemist as well, love?' She gave me a note. I opened it. *1 packet of Mene no 2 please,* it read.

'I don't need a note, Mum, I can remember that.'

'No, take it – it might be a man serving. Oh, I nearly forgot.' She moved over to the sideboard. 'This package came for you.'

'Me?' I asked. 'A package for me?' Wide eyed, I gazed at the brown wrapping paper and the typed address label: Miss Jacqueline M. Campbell.

Mum watched as I carefully opened the package.

'Don't tear the paper,' she said. 'I might need it someday.'

My mouth dropped open when I saw the contents. It was a set of Reeves Watercolour Paints.

'Mum, look at this.'

'Who's sent you that?' Her face beamed as I read the letter.

Dear Miss Campbell, Thank you for entering our recent Horniman's Tea competition…'

'It's that painting competition I entered ages ago – I'd forgotten all about it. I've come third.' I danced around the table, hugging the letter and tin of paints. I was so happy. I'd actually won something, proper paints.

* * * *

The following day was Saturday. I was skinning the rabbits Dad had brought home yesterday teatime. I chopped off the heads and legs, removed the guts and cut through the tough bits with the bacon scissors.

'Here, while you've got the scissors handy, just cut the back of my hair, will you, Jack?' asked Dad, unbuttoning his shirt collar and tucking it inside.

'Wait a minute. I'll just put these to soak.' I placed the rabbits in an enamel bowl and covered them with water and a bit of salt.

'They look meaty,' said Dad, as I placed them in the pantry.

I collected the remains of the rabbits, threw them into the fire and rinsed the scissors under the tap. I placed the towel around Dad's neck.

Dad didn't believe in going to the barber. Bald on top, he thought he should get a discount and reckoned that as I could handle a pair of scissors, I could easily manage his hair.

'Is your mother around?' he asked when I'd finished.

'No, she's upstairs making the beds.'

'Good, get her sewing scissors out of her box and trim these whiskers out of my ears and nose, it's like a forest up there.'

I took the small scissors and began trimming.

'Be quick,' he said. 'If she comes down and sees us using her scissors, she'll have a fit.'

There was a knock on the door, and Uncle Jack appeared, without waiting for us to let him in.

'Anybody in?' He came inside. 'Has that kettle boiled?' he asked, in the same breath. Uncle Jack placed his workbag on the floor.

'It'll not be a minute. I'm just finishing Dad's trim.'

'Aye, it's okay, lass – you finish what you're doing.' He shook the kettle before lighting the gas. He emptied the old tea leaves out of the pot and replaced them with new ones.

'How's Charlie then?' He looked over at Dad.

'Not bad. Could be better, could be worse, but thankful for how I am.' Dad fastened up the neck of his shirt as I took away the towel and shook it in the fire.

'That's the spirit, Charlie,' said Uncle Jack. The kettle whistled and he made a pot of tea. 'Where's our Margaret?'

'Upstairs making the beds. She'll be down in a minute.'

He poured tea for me and Dad, then took a white pint pot mug from his workbag and filled it to the top, added four teaspoons full of sugar and stirred.

'It's a good job rationing's finishing,' said Mum as she came downstairs and went over to her brother, kissing him on the cheek.

'Ey up, lass. How's my favourite sister?' He took a large slurp of his scalding hot tea and reached up on the mantel shelf for a taper, pushed it into the fire and lit a stub of a cigarette, taken from behind his ear.

'Get away with you, you say that to all of us. I hope this isn't just a social call,' said Mum, as she poured a cup for herself.

'Nay, not this time, lass.' He coughed and spat in the fire. 'I've come to strip the doors for you, you've been on about it for long enough. I've brought a bit of plaster to patch them holes up in the ceiling as well.' He took a few quick drags on his cigarette and threw it in the fire.

'I'd better move out of the way, then.' Dad rose from his chair. 'Landlord's supposed to be coming to do the repairs in a couple o' weeks, but he's said that before and never turned up. Never misses collecting the rent though.'

'You stay put, Charlie. I can work round you. The morning paper's in my bag if you'd like to take a look at it.' He took the paper over to Dad, and pulled on a pair of white overalls, covered in splashes of mostly green paint as he worked for the council.

'I see Churchill's made it to eighty then,' said Dad, reading from the newspaper.

Uncle Jack looked at him. 'Aye – 'e can afford it. Right, Jacqueline, are you going to help? I hear you're good with a brush.' He laughed and then had a coughing fit.

'Can I?' My eyes lit up at the thought of some serious painting.

He adjusted the metal fasteners on the braces of his overalls, and primed his blowlamp, pumping it up and down with one hand, while manoeuvring a cigarette out of the packet in his bib pocket with his other. He placed it between his lips and held the lamp towards the fire until it caught light, then adjusted the flame and lit his cigarette. You could tell he had done this many times before, as the front of his hair and eyebrows were singed.

With the blowlamp pointing towards the door, he scratched away at the melting paint with a scraper.

'I hear you've been winning some prizes for painting. Proper little Picasso, eh?'

I nodded, pleased that someone else knew.

'Which do you want to do, hold the blowlamp or the shave hook?'

'Is that what it's called?' I looked at the triangular-shaped metal tool with the wooden handle. 'I'll have a go with that first.'

I stood on a paint-splashed wooden box and scraped away at the paint at the top of the door while he held the blowlamp.

'So, what's with the prizes, then?

'I won a tea competition...'

'Sounds like my cup of tea that.' We both laughed. 'What did you have to do – see who could drink the most tea?'

We laughed again. Uncle Jack's laugh turned into a coughing bout, so he lit a cigarette. The peeling paint fell onto an old newspaper placed on the floor.

'And then I won another prize, for painting a big picture of York Minster to put in the school foyer for the trip. I couldn't go on the trip because of Mum, but the teachers gave me a Lakeland coloured pencils set and a drawing pad instead.'

'Looks like I'll have to get your name down at our place for a job when you leave school.'

'They don't have girls doing your job,' I replied.

'They will when you leave school,' he said. 'You'll be a painter and decorator, you mark my words. That's why they named you after me.'

I stood still and looked at him, then a big grin spread across his face and he laughed.

'You're kidding me.'

'No I'm not – you ask your mam.'

'I know you're kidding. I saw you wink at Mum. Anyway, I'm going to be a doctor.'

'Oh, are you now? Well I'll know where to come when I get a bad chest, eh?'

44

'You've already got one,' I said, as he started coughing again.

* * * *

We were just finishing the door when Mum came over.

'Tea for the workers,' she said, as she brought over Uncle Jack's mug and a cup for me. He turned off the blowlamp.

Josie came out from under the table with a picture she had coloured, and her teddy bear tucked under her arm.

'Where have you been hiding?' said Uncle Jack, as he sat on a chair and lifted her up. He tickled her, and then placed her on his knee. She giggled and laughed. Teddy and the picture fell to the floor, as he crossed his legs and placed her astride his shin and held her hands.

'Ride a cock-horse to Banbury Cross…' he sang to her, as he jostled her up and down. She sang along with him and laughed until she screamed for him to stop. He lifted her off and tickled her again.

'I think you've broken my leg,' he said, joking. 'You've put so much weight on since I last saw you.'

She picked up her teddy and the picture and went over to show Mum.

Uncle Jack drank his tea in one gulp, and picked up the blowlamp.

'Might as well fill it up while we're having a break,' he said, then knelt on the floor and opened a tin of paraffin. He poured some into the little cup on the top of the lamp.

'Be careful, Jack,' said Mum, a worried look on her face.

'Stop wittering, lass, I've turned it off.'

'Perhaps so, but you have a cigarette hanging out of your mouth.'

'It's a good job they didn't send the women to the front. We'd have never have won the war.' He looked at me and grinned.

5

A week before Christmas, I brought the tree down from the attic. It looked like a few dark green flue brushes stuck together. Josie and I decorated it with a box of shiny glass baubles and slightly tarnished tinsel. Mum placed a large glass bauble with a long spike on the top of the tree. When it was finished, I placed it in the centre of the sideboard.

We made paper chains by looping together strips of coloured paper, and hung them around the walls. I drew pictures of snowmen, Christmas trees, robins and Father Christmas, for Josie to colour and fold into Christmas cards for her friends. The cards had no envelopes; the girls' names and class numbers were written on the back, and placed in the school post box.

At Sunday school, I drew and painted a large picture of Angel Gabriel and fastened it to the wall. Josie and I made a Nativity scene out of Plasticine, with baby Jesus in his crib surrounded by shepherds and their sheep. From the park, we collected holly, which Josie wouldn't carry because it was too prickly.

* * * *

The doorstep and window-sill had been donkey-stoned, the fireplace black-leaded with Zebo, the lino scrubbed, the windows cleaned and curtains changed. Even the washing lines across the room were temporarily removed. On Christmas Eve, Josie and I went with friends to other houses in the street and sang carols, where we were given mince pies or humbugs, and sometimes money: pennies or halfpennies. Occasionally, we would get a threepenny bit.

Mum put a mince pie on a plate and a small glass of milk for Father Christmas, with a chopped-up carrot for the reindeers. Two white pillowcases hung off either end of the mantelpiece.

'What time does Father Christmas get here?' Josie asked, while we undressed for bed in front of the fire.

'Not until you're fast asleep,' I replied, and pulled my old cardigan over my nightie.

'What if I can't go to sleep?' A worried look crossed her face.

'You'd better make sure you do, otherwise you'll get no presents.' I brushed her hair.

'Ouch,' she screamed, as I tugged on a lug. 'But I want to see him.'

'You can't – he only lets you see him when he wants to be seen, like when we went to visit him in his grotto in town last week.'

'What if I creep down in the night?' She crouched down low.

'You'll still not see him.'

She jumped up. 'Why not?'

· 'Because it will be dark and you can't reach the light switch! Come on, let's have you off to bed.'

'Only if you'll read me a story.' She chewed the collar of her nightie.

'Okay then, what shall we read tonight?' I put the brush and her ribbons in the sideboard drawer. We turned to go. I glanced at the plate. 'Who's had a bite out of Santa's mince pie?'

She looked away.

* * * *

I awoke the following morning to Josie's excited screams as she came running upstairs and over to the bed, her blue eyes sparkling.

'He's been Jack-Jack, he's been! The glass is empty and the mince pie and carrots are gone.'

'I've got a new dolly and a pram, and she's got some new clothes already. I've got a Mr Potato Head, a Noddy annual, a jigsaw puzzle, some sweets and some pom-pom slippers – come and look Jack-Jack, come on.'

'You're not supposed to look until Mum and Dad are up.' I pulled my cardi over my nightie, and put my feet into my slippers.

'But they are up – they're having a cup of tea.'

'Oh, I was just bringing you a cup of tea, love,' said Mum, from the doorway.

'Thanks, Mum.' I took it off her and got back into bed. Mum sat on the bed and stroked my hair. I placed the tea on the bedside table and gave her a hug.

Josie ran downstairs and re-appeared minutes later. Climbing onto the bed, she pushed the Mr Potato Head set towards me, gave me a hug and emptied the box of parts.

'Make me a funny one, Jack-Jack.'

* * * *

Apart from the Carol Service I could hear on the wireless, there was an unusual silence as I went downstairs. I looked out of the kitchen window. There were no thumping hammers, no vibrating floors, glasses or window panes, and no smoke and soot from the tall chimneys. You could even hear a few birds singing in the yard where Mum had put crumbs out.

My clothes were warming over the fireguard; the fire roared in the grate. At seven weeks old, Ian, his navy blue eyes darting around the room trying to focus, lay in Dad's arms. Dad sat, proudly nursing his young son. A new rattle and a teething ring, which Josie had opened, were on the table nearby, along with some wooden building blocks with farm animal pictures on for when he became older. Mum and Dad were listening to the carols on the wireless, Mum singing and crying along with them as she peeled the onions.

'What have you got?' Josie came over, urging me to open my presents.

'I'd better have a look and see. On second thoughts, I think I'll open them in private.'

'You can't,' she said, pulling the bulging pillowcase towards herself. 'Can I open one?'

'No you can't, they're Jacqueline's not yours,' said Mum. 'You can watch, and don't touch anything unless Jacqueline says you can....are you listening?'

I looked in the pillow case. I was just as excited as Josie while opening my presents, even though I knew the facts about Father Christmas. A John Bull printing set, a Monopoly game, some violet-scented notepaper and envelopes, a jigsaw puzzle, a Girls' Crystal annual, the latest Beano annual, some slippers and some sweets.

'Thanks, Mum – thanks Dad.' I gave them both a kiss and hug.

'It's Father Christmas you should be thanking,' said Josie, as she sat on the rug sniffing the notepaper.

I dressed, toasted a slice of bread on the fire and helped Mum with the dinner. She had bought some beef mince and was just finishing off making a meatloaf, adding breadcrumbs to the mince, sausage meat and chopped onions. I hated the cowheels, sheep's heads, and tripe, our usual diet, so this was a welcome change.

The damper was drawn aside and the oven was hot. I took the meatloaf from her and placed it in the centre of the oven, using a piece of old army coat to push it into place. Dad peeled the potatoes, carrots and sprouts, while I mixed the seasoned pudding; a Yorkshire pudding mixture with some chopped onion and sage added.

A clean linen cloth that Mum had embroidered with tiny crinoline ladies all around the edges, with larger ladies in the corners, covered the kitchen table. Knives and forks were placed in position, rather than piled up in the middle. A bottle of ginger beer stood in the centre, and Mum's best glasses were placed beside each place setting.

When dinner was ready, we sat around the table in our best clothes. Even Mum had changed out of her pinny and was wearing a flowered dress with the string of pearls Dad had bought her for a wedding present. Dad had changed into his best and only suit, the one he'd got married in, and was wearing a shirt and tie. He poured us all a glass of ginger beer.

'God save the Queen,' he said, while standing, and raised his glass. Josie and I giggled, and Mum said grace, then sliced the meatloaf and placed some on our plates, along with the vegetables, seasoned pudding, and gravy. Christmas pudding with custard followed. The best dinner ever.

Ian gurgled away in his pram, and Josie and I played with our toys while Mum and Dad listened to the Queen's speech on the wireless, and then dozed in their chairs by the fire.

* * * *

The bitterly cold weather came with the New Year. The windows had as much ice on the inside as the outside. Three elderly residents in our street died from chest-related illnesses. Thankfully, Dad and I were not affected. Now I was back at school, and trying to catch up, as the scholarship exams were fast approaching. Wednesday was Art and Craft day. The pupils assembled in the room ready for the lesson. The teacher called me to the front.

'Jacqueline,' she said, looking deadly serious. 'We have a project for you. I think you will enjoy it.'

What? I wondered. She pointed around the room.

'We want you to draw with coloured chalks "How We Lived Through the Ages".

Start with the Stone Age and go through the different ages, finishing with the current day – Life in the Fifties.'

My eyes widened. This was so exciting. The upper part of two of the walls was covered in blackboards. Looking at the height and length, I guessed it to be about four feet high and twenty-five feet long. I would have to measure it properly and couldn't wait to tell Mum and Dad.

'But, Miss Cooke, I'll never complete it in one lesson.'

She smiled. 'You won't have to. It is to be completed over the next few weeks. Instead of your regular art and craft lesson, you are to do this instead.'

I began immediately, working out which eras I would cover and how much space I could use for each one. When I had some ideas, I told Miss Cooke about them, who said they were good and to go ahead with them. There was a problem though. The other pupils in the class, who didn't enjoy art and craft lessons, sat lolling on their desks, watching me draw the pictures instead of getting on with their work.

* * * *

When I arrived home, a letter had arrived from the education department, stating a date for me to take an art exam. If I passed the test along with my scholarship exams, I would be going to the College of Arts and Crafts.

'Can I go round to Lynn's and tell her about it?' I asked Mum.

'Yes, but don't be late back.'

'Thanks, Mum, I'll take some comics with me to see if she's any to swap.'

Lynn lived in the next street. House and street the same as ours, row after row after row.

The smell of liquorice and aniseed coming from Bassett's confectionery plant temporary overpowered the acrid smells from the other factories as I skipped along the pavement to her house.

'Where do you take the exam?' she asked.

'At the City Grammar,' I replied. 'But if I pass, I'll be going to The College of Arts and Crafts.

'But why go the College of Arts and Crafts if you're going to be a doctor?'

'I don't know – probably because I'm good at art?' I couldn't think of any other reason.

'I don't think you'll be going anywhere,' she replied. 'When I told

Mum and Dad how clever and good at art you are, they said you might not be going anywhere, as your parents can't afford to send you – the uniforms cost too much.'

I thought about it for a minute. 'Perhaps that's why Mum's talking of going back to work when Ian gets a bit older.'

We left her house, walked across the main road and into the park, then strolled up to the old men's hut. There were no old men in it now; they only sat there during the day, smoking, coughing and spitting, and talking about old times. We sat down on the scarred seats. I looked at the carvings and wondered why people wanted to carve things on them.

'Is your Mum taking up nursing again?' Lynn asked.

Some boys who weren't much older than us came in and lit cigarettes.

'No, she says she's too old to go back into nursing. She's been thinking of going on the twilight shift at Bassett's, seeing as it's only round the corner. Your mum works there, doesn't she?'

'Yes, but she does the mornings. Dad likes to have his tea on the table when he gets home from work in the evenings.'

The lads heard us and turned round.

'Look who it is, then,' said one of them. 'If it isn't Deaks and Campi.'

They were trying to look tough with the cigarettes dangling from their lips, but they kept dropping them as they spoke and their eyes were watering. We laughed, The Mob, in short trousers. The one who'd spoken stood with his coat open and hands in trouser pockets, eyes squinting with the smoke.

'What's this?' said another snotty-nosed kid. He pulled the bundle of comics from under my arm.

'Girls' Crystal, School Friend.' He laughed and started tearing them up. The others joined in.

'Wouldn't wipe my arse on these, would you, lads?'

'Come on, let's go,' said Lynn. 'It's starting to stink in here.'

We got up to leave, as globs of spit landed behind us.

* * * *

It wasn't quite dark, so we went round the streets, knocking on doors and asking for jam jars. We only collected six. The shopkeeper gave us threepence for them, which we spent on his penny tray.

We were chewing away on Black Jacks and Fruit Salads when we turned the corner into the street. Harry Atkins and Alan Bates were kneeling on the ground, playing marbles in the fading light. They too wore short trousers, showing scabby knees. Their long grey socks flopped around their ankles and dirty pullovers were stretched over frayed-neck shirts. They both lived in our street and were the same age as Lynn and I.

They stood up when they saw us.

'Any sweets left?' Alan asked, forcing my hand open. He wiped his nose on his shirtsleeve. Harry forced Lynn to open hers.

'None left, Harry,' she said. 'But you can have this one.' She spat the one in her mouth at him, hitting him on the nose. We set off running, but they caught up with us and twisted our arms right up our backs.

'Get off,' we cried.

'Where'd you get the money from?' Alan pushed my arm further up my back.

'We took some jam jars back to the shop. Now let go.' My arm and shoulder hurt.

'There'll be none left for us then,' said Harry. 'Better break their arms, Alan, that'll stop 'em.'

Mr Bates, Alan's Granddad, came round the corner. 'What's going on here then?' He gave Alan an angry look.

They let go of our arms.

'Nothing, Granddad,' Alan replied. 'We're only playing.' A big smirk crossed his face. Lynn and I rubbed our arms, trying to get some circulation back into them.

'Well bugger off home, I'll tell your father about this when I see him,' Mr Bates warned. He looked at Lynn and me. 'And you two.

Haven't you anything better to do than hang about with these daft buggers?'

'We're just going, Mr Bates, thank you.'

He turned down the entry and didn't come back.

'Come on,' said Stanley to Alan. 'Let's go and raid the beer-off yard and see how much we can get.'

We set off, walking in the opposite direction.

'They'll not get owt there,' said Lynn. 'Our Walt went round earlier, says Old Tom's had the yard covered in. Fed up of the kids climbing over the wall and pinching his empties, then taking 'em into the shop and collecting the deposits.'

6

Early spring and the snow had gone – what bit we had. There were too many chimneys that melted it before it hit the ground. Our share always turned to slush.

It was a teachers' rest day and a Friday. I had been down to Dad's works for his wages, and was now doing the weekly grocery shop for Mum. Pushing the big pram with Ian snuggled up inside and Josie holding on to the side handle, we sang nursery rhymes as we walked to the Co-op. Josie had wanted to take her dolly and pram, but I'd said no.

'You'll only get tired and want carrying, and then what will we do with your pram?'

'But I'll not get tired,' she argued.

'Okay, if you do get tired, we'll just have to leave it behind, and come back for it another day. If I was a dolly, I wouldn't want to be left outside in the dark without my mummy at night.'

She thought for a moment, and then went over to her pram.

'I'm going shopping with Jack-Jack, I'll come back soon, Susie,' she said, and tucked a cover around the doll.

* * * *

'Higgledy Piggledy my black hen…' Josie was still singing as I parked the pram outside the shop with the other prams and babies. I took hold of her hand and we went inside and joined the queue. Mrs Glaves stood in front. She turned and smiled.

'Hello, Jacqueline, how's your baby brother coming along?' I haven't seen much of your mum since she had him. Mind you, the weather hasn't been too good for getting about, has it? I know she had a bad time with the baby. Is your dad all right now, love? I hear he's been suffering with his chest again. Terrible, all the smog we get round here. And look at your Josephine there – she's a bonnie girl if ever there was...'

I never got the chance to reply. Mrs Glaves turned as the assistant shouted "Next".

Another assistant came along shortly afterwards. I handed over the grocery book and purse, and then waited while the girl behind the counter studied the list. She sliced the bacon, cut the cheese, weighed the sugar, flour, margarine and lard, and the broken biscuits. The assistant collected the tinned and ready-packed food and placed it all on the counter. She entered a price by the side of each item on the list. When she had finished, she counted out the milk cheques, and added it all up.

'What's your divi number, love? Your mam's not put it on.'

'19532,' I replied.

'Can I have a biscuit, please?' Josie asked, as she tried to climb onto the bag shelf attached to the front of the counter.

'Wait a minute,' said the assistant, smiling at Josie. She added up the list again, and took it over to an older woman for checking. The woman took the five-pound note from the purse and put it into a metallic container with a copy of the total price and Mum's divi number. She pressed a button, and, with a loud rush of air, the capsule whizzed around the store on a track and vanished into the ceiling. A few minutes later, it returned. The woman removed the lid, put the change into the purse, and fastened its press-stud.

'I'll help you with that,' the assistant said as she came round to the front to help put the groceries in the shopping bags. She then helped to place the bags under the pram on the wire shelf. There were too many items, so some had to go into the pram with Ian.

'What about a biscuit?' Josie asked again.

'Stop that,' I said. 'You're being naughty and rude. You wait until you're given one.'

'But she might forget.'

The assistant and I laughed as she handed me the purse.

'You put that somewhere safe,' she said. 'And tell your mum we hope she gets well soon.' She pulled a biscuit from her overall pocket and gave it to Josie.

Josie's eyes widened. 'Thank you,' she said, and ate the biscuit as we set off for home. Five minutes later, she stopped. 'Jack-Jack, I'm tired, carry me.'

* * * *

Josie woke up when we arrived home. I lifted her off the front of the pram, pulled it over the doorstep and placed the groceries on the table. Mum began to check the items against the prices written in the book.

I got the old leather potato bag from under the pram.

'I'm just going round to the fruit shop, Mum – I didn't get anything with Josie being on the pram so I'll go now.'

'Okay, love. Have you got some money?'

I retrieved Mum's purse from where it had been tucked into the pram mattress by Ian's side, and took half a crown out.

'I'll not be long.'

* * * *

Mr Green took a small tin of Top Mill snuff from his waistcoat pocket. He opened it, dipped his thumb and forefinger into the brown powder, and then pushed some up each nostril. He took a couple of sniffs and replaced the tin back in his pocket.

'Ahh, that's better. Now then, young lady, what can I get you?'

'Hello, Mr Green. Five pounds of King Edwards, please.'

I always wondered if it was his real name or one he used just for the shop. He lit a cigarette; it dangled from his lips as he pushed his hands into the sack of potatoes. I held my bag open while he dropped them in. He repeated his actions, grabbing two more large handfuls of potatoes and dropping them in the bag, along with an extra one.

'A pound of carrots and onions, and a turnip please.'

He breathed heavily as he bent down to the lower shelves.

'How's your mother? I've not seen her for ages now.' He dropped the carrots and onions into the bag, along with the ash off his cigarette, followed by an earth-covered turnip.

'She'll be coming out more now the weather's picking up,' I said.

'That's good. Tell her I've asked after her. Is that all?'

'Have you got any damaged fruit for a penny?'

'I'll have a look for you.' He poked around under the counter. 'There, how's that?' He stuffed a couple of apples, a pear and an orange into the bag.

'Thank you, Mr Green. Mum will be pleased.'

'That'll be one and seven, love.'

I handed him the half crown. A wooden bowl stood on the back of the counter where he placed the coins. He pulled a brown, stained handkerchief from his pocket and wiped his nose.

'You look after that mum o' yours,' he said, stuffed the hanky back in his pocket, and passed me the change.

'I will, Mr Green. Thank you, goodbye.'

* * * *

'I've ironed your skirt and blouse for tomorrow,' said Mum, when I returned. 'And there's a clean cardigan on the bed.'

'I don't have to take anything tomorrow, do I? I asked, and put the vegetables and fruit in the pantry.

'I don't think so, love. I'm sure everything will be provided. You'll have to take a sandwich though. Do you want some of that Spam you brought?'

'Yes, please.' I lifted Ian from his pram and changed his nappy, then mixed his feed, but he didn't want it. He kept pulling away from the teat and crying.

'He's started teething already, and he's not happy about it,' said Mum, and took a bottle of Nurse Harvey's mixture out of the cupboard. She poured out a teaspoonful and handed it to me. I slowly poured the mixture into his tiny mouth. He became quiet, but then started howling again.

'Can I go out and play, Mummy?' asked Josie. She held a whip and top in her hand.

'Yes but don't go out of the street, and look out for the lorries coming in and out of the works yard.' Mum opened the door for her and Josie skipped past the window.

* * * *

I wasn't really nervous about taking the exam, even though I'd bitten my nails right down to the quick whilst on the tram into the city. I wasn't late either, even though the tram connector had come off its track and the driver had to get out and fasten it back on with a long pole he carried for such happenings.

My feelings changed when I saw the other pupils, boys and girls. They were dressed very smartly. I looked down at my plaid skirt with shoulder straps fastened to the front with two odd buttons, and my bright yellow blouse, bought from last week's jumble sale at the Methodist church hall. I became aware of my cardi, with the elbows darned in a slightly different colour. It had looked the same in the light at home. My sandals, with the buckle straps obviously replaced.

Most of the other pupils carried leather satchels, and their mothers were with them, even some dads. The parents fussed, telling them what to do and what not to do. They were looking in and out of their satchels, pulling out pencils, crayons, paints, brushes and measuring devices.

'I don't think so, everything will be provided.' Mum's words came back to me. I carried only my tram fare home and a Spam sandwich wrapped in greaseproof paper. No one spoke.

* * * *

I wanted to run, wanted to go home where I belonged, with Mum and Dad and Josie and Ian. They were my world. I didn't want to be with these people.

Then I saw Jean Rockwell and Susan Springer. They were in my class. They came over, both with their mothers.

'Are you scared, Jacqueline?' Jean asked, her hands fidgeting. Her mother stood by her side, smoothing Jean's hair.

'I feel sick,' said Susan, and felt in her pocket for her handkerchief. She looked pale.

'Now, have you got everything?' Her mother fussed, and looked in her satchel. 'What about you, Jacqueline, isn't your mother with you?'

I didn't get chance to reply.

'No, Mum, Jacqueline's had to have a lot of time off school because of her mother being poorly,' said Susan.

Both mothers looked at each other.

'Where's your satchel, Jacqueline?' Mrs Rockwell asked.

'I haven't got one.' I replied, and raised my hand, showing my wrapped sandwich and tram fare.

'Well, what are you going to draw with?' they asked.

I wanted to run away more than ever.

'Mum said they would be provided.'

'She can use some of mine,' said Jean.

'And mine,' echoed Susan. 'We've got more than enough.'

'Yes, let's make sure we sit near each other,' Jean added.

A man came up the corridor. He looked very stern.

'Have all pupils been to the lavatory? If not, go now, as you will not be allowed out once the exam has started.' He waited a few moments.

Silence flowed down the corridor. No one moved.

'Will all pupils sitting an exam please follow me? All parents please leave the building.'

The parents kissed their children goodbye, wished them luck, and walked away, waving and sniffling into handkerchiefs.

We followed the man down the corridor until he suddenly stopped.

'All boys who are taking Technical Drawing, please go into this classroom.' Apart from a man in a suit holding a batch of examination papers, the room was empty.

'The rest of you follow me.'

We followed him into another classroom.

'I presume the rest of you are taking the Arts and Crafts exam.' He looked us over. 'Your seats and desks are assigned. Find which is yours and sit down.'

Jean, Susan and I looked at each other as we walked around the desks, trying to find our places. There were fifteen desks, all in a semi-circle, so everyone would be of an equal depth to the object. After a lot of scuffling with desks and chairs scraping on the wooden floor, we finally sat down. We were not together.

'You will see on your desk a sheet of cartridge paper, a HB pencil, a sharpener and an eraser.' He pulled back a curtain to reveal a two-wheeled bicycle. 'You are to sketch this. No drawing implements must be used, other than the pencil. The use of any other device will result in disqualification.'

I looked at the bike. I hadn't drawn anything like this before. Most of the things I drew could be coloured in: buildings, people, animals, clothes, trees and flowers. I glanced around at the other pupils: fifteen heads deep in thought.

'Right, get your sniffs and coughs out of the way and then I want absolute silence,' he said. 'I want to hear a pin drop in this room.' He held his thumb and forefinger up in the air. I assumed there was a pin in it, but couldn't be sure. I then heard the tiniest of noises and he bent down to retrieve the pin. 'Begin.'

* * * *

'I thought it was a hearing test when he dropped the pin,' laughed Jean, as we sat in the schoolyard eating our sandwiches at lunchtime.

what we'll get this afternoon,' I said.

the other pupils came over and asked what school we
att___ e exchanged details. They were surprised to learn that we
didn't attend a mixed school. We asked how they got on with boys in
class. A unanimous decision: boys were horrible. We drank water
from the fountain, and made our way back to the classroom.

The bicycle had gone and in its place, an elderly man sat in a chair.
He had grey hair and was wearing a suit and tie, spectacles, and held a
pipe to his mouth. We had to draw a semi-side profile, and to be sure
to shade in all the detail. I had no difficulty drawing the man, but his
spectacles didn't look right and my paper began to look grubby with
all the rubbing out. I noticed some of the others rubbing out a lot as
well. By the end, pleased with my drawing, I was ready for home and
a cup of tea.

We came back together on the tram and talked about what it
would be like at the new school, sure we would pass, and how smart
we would look in our uniforms, especially as we'd never had to wear
them before.

'You've got to pass your scholarship exam first,' said Mrs
Springer. 'It's only a week away.'

'I'm alright with arithmetic and writing, it's the problem solving
that worries me,' said Susan.

'Me too,' Jean and I replied.

The journey passed in no time.

'Parkside Road,' the conductress shouted.

I thanked Mrs Rockwell for paying my fare, said goodbye and
made my way to the platform. I jumped off just before it stopped and
waved to the others as the tram rattled away. I still had my tram fare
in my pocket so I called in at the corner shop and bought some
sweets from the penny tray for Josie and me.

* * * *

Whitsuntide: a special time and as exciting as Christmas. It was the only time in the year when we got a complete new set of clothes. We couldn't wait for Whit Sunday, when we would visit the neighbours.

'We've come to show you our new clothes.'

'Turn around,' they'd reply, smiling, and would give us a few coins. We put the money away until the following day when all the families met up in Hillsborough Park.

The churchgoers marched in parades, holding large banners. The band played on the bandstand, and all our cousins, aunties and uncles would get together. We'd go on the paddle boats, and roly-poly down the hills, and then get a scolding from Mum for the grass stains on our new clothes. Returning home, we whitened our sandals and placed them outside on the window-sill to dry.

* * * *

This year, Mum said I was growing up and was too old for a frilly dress. We were in Blanchards on Infirmary road, when the assistant, wearing traditional black dress, brought a monstrosity from out of a back room.

'What about this one, Mrs Campbell? New stock, only came in yesterday. Your Jacqueline will look beautiful in this. Not that she doesn't look beautiful already – a proper young lady – she'll be leaving school before you know it.'

Leaving school? I hadn't even gone into the seniors yet. I couldn't believe my ears, or eyes: surely Mum wouldn't put me in that. It was a horrible salmon-pink costume; a two-piece suit with a long pleated skirt and double-breasted jacket.

'But, Mum,' I protested. 'It's miles too big.'

'It's not, try it on.' Her eyes widened and she nodded.

'Come on, love, slip off your skirt and blouse and your liberty bodice, you'll not be wearing that by Whitsuntide.'

Reluctantly, I slipped off my clothes, and stood in front of the counter in just my vest and navy blue knickers. The assistant disappeared into the back room again and returned with a pink candyfloss of a dress.

'What about this for Josephine?' she drooled.

Josie's eyes lit up. 'Ooh yes, Mummy, let me try it on.' She danced around, holding Mum's hand, and then started undressing, while jumping up and down.

My eyes were downcast as I put on the horrible suit. Josie's eyes were like sparkling sapphires as she twirled around in front of the mirror. The dress fitted her perfectly.

Mum looked at her and smiled, then looked at me.

'Mmm! It does look a bit on the big side.'

A bit on the big side. 'Mum, it's massive,' I pleaded.

'We can do alterations for a small charge,' said the assistant. She began tucking up the sleeves that hid my fingertips from view. 'Don't forget, she'll soon grow into it.'

When I'm fifteen, I thought.

'About four inches off the sleeves and hem of the skirt should do it.' She knelt down and put a couple of pins in the hem.

'Four inches?' I glared at them. 'It'll still be round my ankles.' I looked down.

'Stop sulking,' said Mum. 'You're too old for frilly dresses.'

'I agree with your mum, Jacqueline. You need something more grown up, and this costume is perfect for you.'

'How much is it?' Mum asked. 'Because she'll need a new blouse to go with it.'

'No, I'll not,' I muttered.

'Now, stop that.' Mum shook my shoulders. 'There are plenty of children in this world without any clothes.'

'Well they can have this.' I began taking it off, got dressed and looked at Josie prancing around in front of the mirror.

'Look Jack-Jack, I'm a fairy princess.'

'No you're not, you're too fat to be a princess.'

Mum sighed and looked at the assistant.

'She'll come round.'

'Kids of today, eh, don't know when they're well off. Will that be all, Mrs Campbell?'

'I've got a five pound cheque, so I might as well use it up. I'll have some new vests and knickers for them, plus some long-johns and vests for Charlie.'

'I say, if it wasn't for that cheque company Paget's, the kids round here wouldn't get any new clothes,' the assistant said.

'It's a blessing in disguise,' Mum replied. 'As long as you keep paying them back week by week, you're all right.'

'Trouble is, love, by the time you've paid one off, it's time to take out another.'

They both laughed. I nipped Josie's arm.

* * * *

We were all getting nervous about the scholarship exam. I and a few more school friends were in Lynn's house, discussing our chances of passing.

'They're building a new school at Foxhill for us if we don't pass,' said Sandra Wragg.

'Never,' we replied in unison, and looked at each other.

'How do you know that?'

'My Dad works in the planning office in Sheffield. I heard him tell Mum about it the other night.'

'So what's going to happen to Hillsborough School?' Jean asked.

'It's going to be just for infants and juniors. The seniors will be going to the new school, and that's not all. Listen to this.' She lowered her voice and her head. We moved closer.

'It's going to be MIXED.'

We all sat back.

'Mixed?' we echoed.

'Never! Well I'm not going to a mixed school.' Susan said, and I agreed.

'Listen,' said Jean, 'If we pass our scholarships, we'll be going to mixed schools anyhow, so what difference does it make?'

'Hmm…' We thought about it.

'Well I'm not sitting next to Harry Atkins and Alan Bates,' Lynn snapped.

'Me neither, nor Jim Pickles,' I replied.

'He'll have to have a desk on his own, he's so fat,' laughed Lynn.

'Oooh, and what about Barry Lawton? He's always picking his nose and the scabs on his knees.'

'Come on now, girls,' Lynn's Mum came into the room and went over to the oven.

'Jud'll be here soon and he'll not want you lot hanging around while he has his tea.'

We swapped comics and went home to tell our parents what we had heard.

* * * *

A young married couple called Audrey and Frank had moved into the bottom house in our yard. They had a four month old baby boy. Once they'd got to know us, they asked if I would babysit for them on Friday nights. I loved their baby, Simon, and they were going to pay me a shilling a night.

The following Friday, I went to their house at seven o'clock.

'You look lovely, Audrey,' I said, as she opened the door. She wore a floral dress, beige high-heeled shoes and lace gloves.

I stepped inside and couldn't believe my eyes. It was so modern, just like in the magazines. The inside doors didn't have the usual inset four panels; they had been covered with hardboard and painted duck egg blue. They had sloping chrome and pearl handles. The wallpaper had a pale cream background, overlaid with flowers in pastel shades of blue, ochre and tan, edged with a faint black line. A beige-coloured tiled fireplace fitted to the back wall held a gas fire, and a separate cooker with an oven stood in the corner. An electric washing machine with a wringer attached stood beneath the window.

They didn't have a large wooden table and odd chairs like ours;

they had a shiny plastic one with narrow chrome legs and matching chairs which slid beneath the table when not in use. The set was so compact, there was room for a two-seater settee in front of the gas fire.

'Simon's up here, Jacqueline,' Audrey said, and led me upstairs. The staircase had an edge-to-edge carpet. As we climbed, I noticed she wore nylon stockings with seams up the back.

'Your house is lovely, Audrey; I wish ours looked like this.'

'It will be one day, when your mum goes back to work.'

We crept into their bedroom, which had a highly polished bedroom suite and a crimson satin eiderdown on the bed. I peered at Simon, asleep in his cot. We crept back out.

'I'll leave the bedroom door open and then you'll hear if he cries.'

Geoff, wearing his wedding suit, waited downstairs. His eyes were bright and shining on their first evening out since the birth of Simon.

'There's a bottle of Tizer and some crisps on the table. We'll be back about ten,' he said, opening the door for Audrey as she fastened her coat. What a lovely couple, I thought, as they closed the door behind them. They reminded me of my cousin Brenda and her boyfriend Len.

I sat down on the settee and opened my knitting bag. The needles clicked as I followed the pattern, the ball of blue wool on the sofa beside me. I was making a cardigan for my teddy. He was ten now, the same age as me. I had knitted about ten rows when the light went out. Not just the room light, but the landing light as well. I felt my way to the outer door and opened it. All the house lights in the yard were off. I looked down the entry and saw a faint glow, the street gas lamp, no use to me as it was at the top of the street.

I felt my way back into the house and I could hear Simon crying. Oh no, not now, I thought. Feeling my way upstairs, I found my way to the cot. Not wanting to carry him downstairs in the darkness, I felt for his little body beneath the blanket and picked him up. Wrapping his blanket around him, I rocked him in my arms, and then I heard Mum's voice calling me.

'Jacqueline, are you up there?'

I saw a faint glow and walked to the top of the stairs. Mum came up with a candle in one of her brass candlesticks.

'Is he alright?' she asked, holding the candle nearer so she could see.

He quietened as his eyes focused on the glow. We both agreed he was okay and after a few minutes, he started snoring softly.

I placed him in his cot and we went downstairs.

'Look at this place, Mum, isn't it beautiful?' I said as she moved the candle, lighting up all the areas.

She looked around.

'Here, I'll leave this with you.' She placed the candle on the table, gave me a kiss on the cheek and left.

The lights came back on just before Audrey and Geoff returned.

'What happened?' they asked, when they saw the candle on the table.

'Mum brought it in for me. We had a power cut. All the houses in the street were in darkness.'

'There's some candles and matches in the pantry,' said Geoff, as Audrey went upstairs to check on Simon.

'I didn't like to look, it would be like snooping,' I said.

He pulled me towards him and gave me a hug. He smelled of beer.

'You're a good girl Jacqueline, and you'll make some man very happy one day.'

I felt my face go red and looked away.

Audrey came back downstairs.

'He's still fast asleep. Thank you so much, Jacqueline, we've really enjoyed going out tonight.' She looked at Geoff and smiled, then blushed as he raised one eyebrow, winked and looked towards the stairs. 'I hope you'll come again for us.'

'Oh I will, you know how I love your Simon.' I picked up my knitting and Mum's candlestick from the table.

'Oops! Nearly forgot,' said Geoff as he opened the door. He pressed two shillings in my hand.

I looked at the two silver coins.

'But Geoff, there's two shillings here,'

'You take it, love, you've earned it.'

'Thank you so much.' Two shillings, all mine.

He watched as I walked past the other two houses to our door, and waved goodnight.

I took Josie into Sheffield on the tram the next morning. We went into Woolworth's and bought some comics, Plasticine, a ready printed colouring book, and some sweets.

* * * *

On the day of the scholarship exam, I awoke with a terrible sore throat and headache. Opening the curtains, I looked out across the works yard at the stockpiles of blue-grey steel ingots and bars on pallets stacked all over the yard, yellow and orange with rust. I looked up at the ever-smoking chimneys and the pouring rain.

'Is it time to get up, Jack-Jack?' Josie asked, rubbing the sleep from her eyes.

I turned towards her.

'No, not yet. You can stay in as long as you want, there's no school for you today.' My throat burned with the effort.

I heard Dad coughing in the next bedroom. He had bronchitis again, and had been awake most of the night.

'Stay there, Charlie,' I heard Mum say. 'You're no good in yon cemetery, and that's where you'll finish up if you don't do what the doctor says.'

I pulled on my clothes, and went into their bedroom. 'Is everything okay?' Dad looked terrible.

'It's your Dad, he's insisting on going to work.'

'Do what Mum and the doctor say, Dad.' I sat on the side of the bed and listened to his wheezing chest. 'Please don't go, Dad.' I took hold of his hand, but he let go as he broke into a coughing bout, which turned him blue in the face. He leaned over the side of the bed and spat thick green and black phlegm into the bucket. Breathless, he laid his head back down, gasping.

'I'll go and make some tea,' I said. Ian began to cry.

'Oh no!' I cried, as I went downstairs and found there had been a soot fall during the night. I looked at the blackened clothes hanging over the fireguard and the soot-covered pegged rug in front of the hearth. Where would I start?

Mum came downstairs.

'Good heavens,' she cried, as she looked at the mess. 'The chimney sweep's due next week,' she tut-tutted, and laid Ian in the pram, who immediately started screaming. I made his bottle and a pot of tea.

'Here, drink this. Might as well have a cuppa before we begin,' I said. I rubbed my throat and passed her the cup. 'Does Dad want anything?'

'No, I'll see to him, you get some breakfast. You've a busy day ahead.'

'I don't want anything, just a cup of tea will do. I'll clean this up first and then see what time I've got.'

Mum looked at me and felt my forehead.

'Don't say you're starting with it,' she said, and took the thermometer out of the cupboard, shook it and placed it under my tongue. 'You've got a temperature,' she said, after a couple of minutes.

'I will have, I've just had a drink of tea.'

She took it again after a few minutes. 'It's still the same.'

'I'll be okay, Mum, honest.'

* * * *

The clean-up took longer than I thought and I was late. Running to school, my chest was on fire when I arrived.

DO NOT ENTER – EXAMINATION IN PROGRESS. I read the notice on my classroom door and peered through the small window. A boy sat at my desk. There were boys sitting at all the desks. I felt sick as I realised my mistake, and ran to the boys' school higher up the road. Running along the empty corridors, all the classrooms were empty, and then I saw one with an identical sign on the door.

I peered through the window. I didn't recognise the teacher, but I recognised the girls from my class sitting at the boys' desks. There was one empty desk.

DO NOT ENTER…

Not knowing what to do, I waved at the window, hoping to get the teacher's attention. He wasn't looking. I gave a tiny knock on the door, and looked to see if he had heard. He hadn't, but Susan Springer had, and told the teacher.

He came over and looked annoyed as he pulled the door open and closed it quietly behind him. 'Yes?'

'I'm sorry I'm late, sir, I'm Jacqueline Campbell.' I suddenly became aware of how scruffy I looked from cleaning up the soot. My hair and clothes were wet with the rain. My stomach rumbled, my chest was on fire, and my heart pounded. I felt so ill.

He looked me over and then at his watch, 'It's too late, I'm afraid. The exam has started.'

'Please sir, I must.'

He shook his head.

'I'm sorry, Jacqueline, but I can't have any interruptions while the exam is in progress.'

'But, sir, I'll be able to catch up, honest,' I pleaded and began to cry.

He looked up and down the corridor.

'Oh, come on then, but don't make a noise. Creep over to that empty desk. Your test papers are on it.'

He opened the door and ushered me in. My sandals squelched on the wooden floor as I made my way to the empty desk and turned the top paper over. I sat on the seat and glanced down at the examination papers and across at the other girls, their heads down, hands and pens busy writing.

Picking up the pen, I dipped it into the inkwell and wrote my name across the top. The tummy rumbling worsened and a feeling of light-headedness came over me. I could hardly breathe; my chest felt thick and heavy. I'd had no breakfast, felt faint and badly needed to go to the lav.

I looked at the clock on the wall. Over an hour to go. I daren't ask to be excused, but couldn't wait, and then I heard it. The girls around me raised their heads and listened. The trickle of liquid ran down the grooves on the chair seat and onto the wooden floor. I stood up and raised my hand.

'Please, sir.'

I felt myself falling.

7

'I think we'll have your hair cut now you'll be in the Seniors, give you a new style?'

I turned my head to the side as I looked in the mirror, my chestnut brown hair almost to my waist. Mum always cut a bit off the bottom when she thought it needed it. I couldn't imagine what I would look like with short hair.

'It will curl beautifully, it's natural,' said Mum.

I remembered my few baby photos. 'How come it's not curly now?' I asked.

'It's too long, the weight's pulling it straight,' she replied.

I picked up a magazine and turned the pages. 'Look, Mum – do you think it would go like that? It's called a Bubble Cut.'

I pointed to a picture of a young model with short curly hair. She sat on a capstan by a harbour, leaning back with one foot raised, her hands grasping her knee. A peacock-blue sleeveless blouse with a flyaway collar covered her upper body. Red shorts, sandals and a small neck-scarf finished the style.

Mum looked at the picture and then at me, 'I don't see why not,' she said, and lifted my hair onto the top of my head with one hand, then stepped back and studied the image. 'I'll book it in for you at Madge Marsdens.'

My new hairstyle looked fab. Lynn liked it so much that she said goodbye to her long locks too. We looked so different with our shorter hair. Mum was right; my hair curled into a mass of dark brown bubbles. Lynn's didn't curl as much but it still looked fab.

It reminded me of when we were younger and used to play at film stars. Lynn was always Doris Day because she had blonde hair and I had to be Esther Williams because mine was dark.

* * * *

The summer holiday came to an abrupt end and I went back to school a week before my birthday. No scholarship passes for me, nor Lynn, Sandra or Christine. We were back at Hillsborough, in the Seniors. Jean Rockwell and Susan Springer had passed and gone to their new school.

We now had a male teacher and I hated him.

'Good morning, Mr. Cornthwaite,' we chanted mournfully one morning.

'Jacqueline Campbell,' he called out. He stared at me.

I raised my hand, 'Sir.'

He stood up. 'Come out here and face the front.'

What had I done? My face burned as I walked towards him.

'Turn and face the class.'

I felt so humiliated.

'Right girls, read aloud. What does it say on Jacqueline's jumper?'

Muffled voices mouthed, 'Bill Haley, sir.'

'What? I can't hear you.' He cupped his hand around his ear.

'Bill Haley, sir,' they said, louder.

He looked towards the window. 'Do any of you know Bill Haley?' He waited a moment. 'Come on, speak up,' he shouted as he looked back at the pupils.

Ann Howard raised her hand. 'I've heard of him, sir.'

'Anyone else?' He looked at the girls. A few raised their hands.

'Do any of you know Bill Haley?'

The hands lowered. 'No sir.'

'So, would you say this is Bill Haley?' I looked up, his finger pointed down over my head.

'No, sir.' The girls giggled.

'Neither would I.' He placed his hands on my shoulders and turned me towards him. 'Go and change it,' he snapped, showering me with spittle.

He was referring to an image transfer given out free with the New Musical Express magazine, which I had ironed onto my jumper the previous night. I ran across the yard to the lavs and turned my jumper back to front, the neck high up my throat and low at the back.

'That's better, sit down,' he said, as I returned to the classroom.

I turned to walk back to my desk. After a few steps, I felt his hand on my shoulder. He span me round to face him, and the class erupted in laughter.

'Go HOME and change it,' he snapped, and pushed me towards the door.

* * * *

Mum was baking and listening to the wireless when I arrived home.

'*No other love have I...*' She sang along with Ronnie Hilton on Housewives Choice.

'What are you doing back so soon?' she said.

'I've got to change my jumper, old Corny says so.' I ran upstairs, found another, and came back down. 'Might as well have a cuppa while I'm here.' I put the kettle on. 'Do you want one, Mum?'

'No thanks, love,' she said.

Ian crawled over, offering me a sticky biscuit squashed in his hand.

'Come here, you little scruff.' I lifted him up and sat him on my knee while I waited for the kettle to boil. Taking a hanky from my skirt pocket, I licked it and wiped his biscuit-covered face.

'There, that's better, I can kiss you now.' I covered his face with kisses.

Ian pulled a face, struggled to the floor, crawled over towards Mum and grabbed hold of her legs.

'I will have a cuppa,' she said as she tipped flour from the packet into a large enamel bowl, cut lard and margarine from slabs and added it to the flour.

'What are you making?' I asked as I poured the tea.

Mum added salt to the mix and began to work it all together.

'Meat and Potato pie and jam tarts,' she replied. 'Get it while you can, I'll not have time for baking when I start work.'

'Don't say that, Mum, we love your baking.' I took a drink of my tea. 'You're not serious about going back to work, are you?'

'Yes, I'm starting at Bassett's next week.' She didn't look up; she continued rubbing the fats into the flour.

'*Oh what a glorious thing to be…*' Arthur Askey's childish voice came over the radio.

'How do they get away with making songs like that?' I said, disgusted.

'Only the same as Bill Haley and Woody Holly – whatever his name is. Some people don't like their music,' Mum replied.

I laughed. 'It's Buddy, not Woody, and neither of them would sing about busy bees.'

Mum added water to the mix, brought it all together and moulded it into a ball.

'What hours will you work, Mum?'

'Five till nine.'

My face dropped. 'Who's going to look after Ian and Josie?'

'You and Dad, who do you think?'

'But what about my homework?'

'You'll manage that. Hadn't you better be getting back to school?' she said, as she flattened the ball of pastry and began rolling it out with an empty milk bottle.

* * * *

It wasn't long before we saw the benefits of Mum working. Removal of the huge black range was first, and a new tiled fireplace similar to Audrey's and Geoff's was put in its place, complete with a gas fire.

Next, a gas cooker with an oven, a geyser for the hot water and an electric washing machine were installed, which made life a lot easier. Uncle Jack came and wallpapered and laid new lino in the kitchen.

Mum and I chopped up the large table in the yard and the chairs were given to the jumble sale. A bright orange and blue Formica-topped table with four matching chairs replaced it.

Thanks to Wigfall's weekly payment plan, we now had a television set. The polished wooden-framed TV had a twelve-inch screen and stood in the centre of the sideboard. Dad couldn't understand why we had to have a "bedstead" aerial on the chimney, instead of the "sweep's brush" aerial fastened to the outside kitchen window frame for the wireless. Especially as every time the wind blew, we lost the picture. We spent more time trying to reset the aerial and tune the television than actual viewing hours.

The twelve-inch TV had entertainment for all of us. Ian loved Andy Pandy and The Woodentops. Josie liked Watch with Mother. I loved Six-Five Special. Mum loved Emergency Ward Ten and Take your Pick. Dad liked Dixon of Dock Green and Sunday Night at the London Palladium.

The first time Dad saw the Queen give her Christmas speech live on TV, he cried. Dad actually watched more TV then anyone, considering he didn't initially want one as they contained cathode ray tubes which were dangerous!

* * * *

Josie began having sleeping problems. It wasn't that she couldn't sleep; she needed too much sleep, and Mum was concerned. At nearly seven years old and almost as tall as I was, Mum thought she might be outgrowing herself. But after a while, Mum became more worried and took her to the doctors, who said that she would probably grow out of it when she reached puberty. To put Mum's mind at rest, he said he would refer her to the hospital for further tests.

* * * *

Lynn and I were amongst the first pupils of Chaucer Secondary Modern, when it opened in the spring of 1958.

How different it was to our old school. Now we had large windows where we could see over the playing fields.

There were purpose-built classrooms for different lessons, a canteen, an indoor gym and indoor washrooms with showers and toilets. We no longer called them lavatories.

Pupils from five different schools came to Chaucer. We had five forms to each year: A, B, C, D, and E.

It was so different from Hillsborough, especially with the mixed classes. I hated it at first, as boys were stupid, but after a while, I began to enjoy their humour. Not all of it though, as they could be quite cruel at times. They were all in long trousers now though, so at least we didn't have to look at their scabby knees. We had to look at their spotty faces instead.

8

Mum and Dad bought me a Timex watch for my thirteenth birthday. I was a teenager, at last. Mum worked at Bassett's during the evenings and I still had to look after Josie and Ian, and do my homework.

Josie still wanted to play school at night, as she didn't have homework, and had decided she was going to be a schoolteacher.

Ian just wanted to play and someone to play with, but Dad fell asleep in his chair every night after having his tea, while reading the evening paper. It wasn't surprising: he still worked full time, and he was sixty eight.

* * * *

One day Mum asked me if I would like to have my own bedroom.

'Where?' I asked.

'The attic.'

'The attic?' I thought for a minute. 'Yes,' I replied, thinking about where I could put my Elvis pictures.

'Ian's too old for his cot, so I thought he could go in with Josie, and you could have your own bedroom.'

The more I thought about it, the more excited I became.

'Let's go up and have a look.'

Mum carried Ian and we climbed the stairs. It was late summer and quite warm. Passing Ian to me, she opened the skylight window, carefully, as it had been known to slide down the roof in the past. Ian looked around curiously. He clung onto me, unsure of these new surroundings. There were black stains and mouldy patches on the wall beneath the window, where the rain leaked in.

'I'll get onto the landlord about getting that fixed before the winter sets in. Then I'll see if our Jack can come and wallpaper it for you.'

'But Mum, I can do it. I helped Uncle Jack when he did the kitchen.'

'You'll never reach over the stairs, love.' She looked over the rail at the winding staircase.

'I can, Mum. I can do it off a plank. There's one in the yard. If I put the steps at the top of the stairs and the plank stretching across from the rail to the steps, I can stand on that. Oh, come on, let's go to Blaskey's down Hillsborough and pick some wallpaper.'

'Hold on a minute – we've got to fix the damp.'

'Oh Mum, that'll take forever.' I sat on the old bed and my heart missed a beat as I slowly sank to the floor with Ian still clutched in my arms. Mum and I laughed and even Ian chuckled when he saw us laughing. I held onto him with one arm and reached out with the other.

'I think a new bed is called for,' said Mum as she pulled me to my feet.

* * * *

I stripped off all the old wallpaper, which came away easily beneath the window, with the old perished plaster. Uncle Jack tested the walls by gently tapping them. I did likewise and more fell off.

While waiting for the landlord to come and re-plaster, I painted the old wooden dresser, actually a chest of drawers with a swing-back mirror fastened on the top. It didn't paint up too well, as I hadn't sanded the polish off properly, and the underlying darkness showed through the white paint. It looked better when I had polished up the brass handles and rubbed the drawers with a candle to stop the screeching when I opening them.

It didn't take long before the room was finished. The landlord repaired the wall and replaced the window. What a transformation, and so much lighter without the soot-ingrained glass. Josie climbed up all the stairs to have a look and climbed onto the new bed, jumping up and down, using it as a trampoline.

'I want to sleep in here,' she said, her bottom lip drooping.

'You have to sleep with Ian until you're older, then you can come up here,' Mum told her.

'But I want to come up here and bring my toys.' Her lip dropped further.

I lifted her up – what a weight. I put her back down and sat on the bed.

'But I want to sleep with you.' She wrapped an arm around my neck and sucked her thumb.

Her sad face reminded me of the time when Mum had married Dad and we'd come to live here. Until then, I had always slept with my cousins at Granddad's house. Sometimes there were six of us in one bed, three at the top and three at the bottom. If I was poorly, I'd had to sleep with Mum and Auntie Doris in a small bed.

The blackout curtains had to be drawn shut at night, which made it very dark. None of that was as frightening as sleeping on my own when I first came to live here. The noises kept me awake and when I did fall asleep, I kept waking up with the sound of the hammers, and would go into Mum and Dad's bedroom and creep into their bed, until I fell asleep, and then Mum would carry me back to my own bed. It happened repeatedly. I don't think I stopped until Josie left her cot and came in with me.

'I know what we'll do,' I said to her. 'What if I wallpaper your bedroom and let you choose your own paper?'

She removed the thumb from her mouth and her eyes shone. 'Can I?'

'And what if I paint that old wardrobe for you and stick some pictures on it?'

She got off the bed.

'Can I have some paper with rabbits on?'

'Yes, let's ask Mum when we can do it.'

* * * *

With a little help and much face wiping, Ian could now handle a plastic spoon while sitting in the high chair. Josie needed no help with cutting up her food. She could also tell the time and tie her own shoelaces. Making sure they had eaten, the dishes were washed and cleared away, I washed myself at the kitchen sink and then went upstairs to get ready. Lynn had heard about a new place called the "Memo", the church Memorial Hall, where every Tuesday evening, the verger provided music and dancing for teenagers.

It cost tuppence and that included tea and biscuits, and a short talk from the vicar. Lynn and I decided to try it. I looked in my wardrobe. The horrible salmon-pink costume, still miles too big, worn once – under duress, still hung in the wardrobe like a side of beef in the butcher's fridge.

I donned a pair of light-blue cropped trousers and a yellow t-shirt with a print of Elvis on the front. I pulled on my red windcheater jacket and flicked the collar up. I wore a pair of red "bumpers". All teenagers had a pair. They had either navy blue or red canvas uppers, with thick white soles. The name came from the fairground dodgem cars, as they looked similar. Lynn came round at half past six wearing identical clothes but in different colours: a blue jacket and red trousers, with navy-blue bumpers.

* * * *

The verger had an electric record player, which he brought into the hall. He played popular music, so we learned to dance to the strains of Bill Haley, Elvis, Buddy Holly, Jerry Lee Lewis and many others. We danced until our feet ached.

Most of the lads stood around, watching and chewing gum. Every now and again, the verger would change the style and play the "Gay Gordons" or the "Boston Two-Step", and try to get everyone to join in.

As the evening wore on, he'd play Patti Page singing 'The Tennessee Waltz', and teach us how to dance to it. The lads and some of the girls hated it and usually went outside for a cigarette.

* * * *

One Friday night, when I wasn't baby-sitting for Audrey and Geoff, Lynn and I decided to go the cinema. She was staying at our house overnight. We were so excited, as she hadn't seen my new bedroom before. We were dancing together down Catch Bar lane, after seeing The King and I.

'*Shall we dance?*' we sang as we whirled each other round and round in the middle of the road, imagining ourselves in large, swirling ball gowns. We held each other close, to prevent ourselves from falling. I felt something sticking into my chest. We separated, and I looked at her.

'Lynn, are you wearing a brassiere?'

'Yes, it's one our Ann's, it's too small for her now, and they don't call them brassieres now, they call them bras,' she replied.

Deep in thought, I carried on walking.

'When did you grow those?'

'They've been growing a bit now.' She handed me a bubble gum.

'I haven't noticed,' I said, looking at the two small bumps on her chest, and then down at my flat chest.

'Mum says I have to wear one, otherwise I will have saggy ones like hers. Don't you wear a bra yet?'

'No,' I said. 'And Mum's never mentioned it.'

* * * *

'Look at all these pictures,' said Lynn, admiring my posters as we went up into the attic.

There were pictures of Elvis, Bill Haley, Buddy Holly, Rock Hudson, and Tab Hunter, all taken from Picturegoer magazine and fastened to the wall with drawing pins. In fact, you could hardly see the wallpaper.

'You can have some if you want – there's more under the bed.'

'I wish I could,' she replied. 'But I've got to share a room with our Ann and Jayne.'

We started to get undressed. She wasn't even wearing a vest – she was wearing a camisole instead.

'That's lovely, Lynn. I wish I wore things like that.'

'That's the best thing about having an older sister – you get to wear their cast offs.'

'I usually have my cousin Brenda's cast offs, but I've not got anything like that.'

Lynn took off her camisole and I looked in awe at her bra, and then she removed it. She had real breasts. I didn't want to take off my vest and show her what I hadn't got.

'Here, try it on,' she said, as she pulled her nightie over her head and passed me the bra.

I turned round, pulled off my vest and slid my arms through the bra straps.

'Will you fasten it for me, please?' I backed myself towards her.

'They're a bit fiddly till you get used to them. There you are, turn round, and let's have a look.'

I turned round, ashamed of the empty cups, the thin cotton fabric stuck to my chest.

'Aw, you probably need a smaller size. I'll see if our Ann's got another.' She blew a bubble with her gum, let it pop, then stuck it on the back of the bed head and climbed in. I looked in the mirror again. Disappointed, I removed the bra and donned my nightie, blew and popped a bubble, removed the gum, switched off the light, and joined her.

Dad brought home a bundle of rhubarb someone had given him at work.

'I'll take some to our Doris,' said Mum. 'We'll never be off the lav if we eat it all.'

It was Saturday afternoon, so we left Dad at home listening to the football match on the wireless. Sometimes Dad still preferred the wireless. Josie didn't want to go; she was engrossed in reading about her namesake, Jo, in *Little Women*.

Mum had sold Ian's big pram and replaced it with a pushchair, which we took in turns to push up the steep hill. When we arrived, Auntie Doris was sitting in a chair, picking the corns on her feet with one of Granddad's old razor blades. Her cigarette dangled from her lips.

'Ouch! You bugger,' she said, as she jumped. A splatter of blood and cigarette ash covered her little toe. Pulling a not too clean hanky from her apron pocket, she fastened it around the toe, and pushed her foot into her shoe.

'What brings you here?' she asked, as she went over to the cooker to put the kettle on and then came over to cuddle Ian.

'Rhubarb – we've got plenty, so thought you could make use of some.' Mum removed the newspaper and handed over the long red and green sticks. Ian reached up to the table. I lifted him out of the pram.

'Just a minute,' said Auntie Doris. She tore off a piece of the newspaper and twisted it into a cone shape. Taking a packet of sugar from the kitchen cabinet, she tipped some into the cone. Ian tottered after her as she broke a stem of rhubarb in half and took one of the pieces over to the sink to wash it.

Ian waited, saliva running down his chin.

'What do I get for it?' She bent down in front of him, holding the bag of sugar and stick of rhubarb, and pursed her lips.

He gave her a kiss, never taking his eyes off the treats. We laughed as he dipped the sour stick into the sugar.

Granddad sat in his chair by the fire, the seat springs long gone. A cigarette was held loosely between his nicotine-stained fingers.

'Well look who it is,' he growled, his voice barely audible. He broke into a raucous cough, which seemed to come up from his toes.

I bent over him and gave him a kiss on the cheek. Granddad only had one eye. He had lost his right one during the First World War. He tilted his face towards me and tried to focus with his remaining clouded eye. His toothless mouth smiled, and bottom lip drooled.

The cigarette slipped from his fingers as he struggled for breath.

'You'll be setting t'house on fire one of these days,' said Auntie Doris, who quickly retrieved it and finished smoking it herself.

'How is he, Doris?' Mum asked, as she went towards him.

'Getting worse. Listen to that chest.'

'Are you all right, Dad?' Mum shouted, and took hold of his shaky hand.

He mumbled something none of us could understand, and then raised his fist to his mouth.

'You're not having any more tea yet, you'll only pee yourself again.' Auntie Doris shouted at him. 'His incontinence is getting worse, and he's getting too heavy to lift.'

'It's a pity our Pat left home. You've no-one to help you now,' Mum said.

'Our Brenda gives a hand when she's in.'

'Where is she – and the kids?'

'Brenda's gone out with her friend and Des's took the young 'uns out for the day,' she replied, as she made a pot of tea. 'Wish he'd taken Dad as well, then it would have been heaven.'

Doris stirred two heaped teaspoonfuls of sugar into a mug of tea and passed it to Granddad.

'What's this here then?' She looked at my chest and the outline beneath my blouse.

I felt my face go red.

'She's taken to wearing a brassiere since her friend began wearing one,' Mum said. 'Lynn gave it to her. Don't ask me why, she's nothing to put in it.'

'Shut up, Mum, and it's not a brassiere, it's a bra,' I snapped.'

Auntie Doris pulled me towards her and gave me a hug. 'You wear it love, if it makes you happy. I carry a purse, even though I've nowt to put in it.'

I looked down at the floor.

'Aww, come here. I'll show you what to do.' She took me over to the sideboard, opened the drawer, pulled out a linen bag and removed two handkerchiefs. She rubbed her eyelid as a spark from the cigarette caught it.

'Here, stuff them in the cups.'

'I can't do that!' I blushed again and stepped back.

'Of course you can, it's what all the film stars do.'

'Is it?' I looked at her. You could never tell when she was kidding.

'Here, try it.'

I took the hankies from her and pushed them into my bra, turning sideways, and looked in the sideboard mirror.

'There, you look just like Jane Russell.' Auntie Doris stepped back, smiled, then went back to the sideboard drawer and took out a red lipstick.

Mum looked at me, and then up at the ceiling and shook her head.

'Just a touch of lipstick and you'll pass as her double. In fact, you could probably get a job as her stand-in,' she added, after smearing the red stuff over my mouth. I pouted my lips as I looked in the mirror again. I couldn't believe the transformation. Goodbye Esther Williams and Doris Day. Lynn and I would now be Jane Russell and Marilyn Monroe.

'Give over, Doris, you'll make her old before her time,' Mum said, pulling out a clean hanky and wiping my mouth.

Granddad suddenly burst out coughing and spilled his mug of tea in his lap.

'Quick Margaret, help me get him out of the chair.'

Mum and Auntie Doris took hold of him beneath his arms. A

strong smell of pee came up from the chair as they raised him. His face turned purple. Mum thumped the middle of his back. A large lump of phlegm came up and he spat it into the fire. His colour began to return and he settled back in the chair. He took a few raspy breaths, and then pushed a narrow strip of rolled up newspaper into the fire and lit another Woodbine.

9

'Are you wearing them for the Memo tonight?' Lynn asked, after I'd shown her the hankies in my bra.

'Why not? We'll both look the same then. Shall we wear jeans or dirndl skirts?'

We decided on skirts with crisp paper nylon underskirts and open-necked blouses. Lynn wore her older sister's. Mine was borrowed from my cousin Brenda.

We had a great night, apart from my hankies dropping out of the bottom of my bra with all the swirling and twirling during the rock and roll dances. I didn't dare to pick them up. The verger found them later, and asked who they belonged to. No one claimed them.

* * * *

My cousin Brenda, Auntie Doris's eldest daughter, came down on Sunday evening with her boyfriend, Len. Brenda was eighteen years old and courting seriously. They often came to see us on Sundays. We played cards, draughts and dominoes; even though Mum thought it wrong to play cards on Sundays.

I liked Len. He was very shy and his face went red and shiny when Josie asked if she could sit on his knee and become her boyfriend. He never knew where to put his hands. Mum, Dad and Brenda laughed at him, which made him more embarrassed. He taught me how to play chess and said Brenda didn't have the head for it. He also showed me how to measure things finer than hair. He worked at British Acheson and once brought an instrument to show me how it worked. It could measure thickness to a thousandth of an inch.

Brenda told me they were to be engaged at Christmas and married in the summer next year. She had seen the ring she wanted in Parkers the jewellers, a three stone diamond twist on a plain gold band. I looked down at my hand and imagined how a diamond ring would look on my finger.

'Not very nice with nails like that,' said Brenda. 'Haven't you got any bitter aloes to put on them?'

I crossed my wrists and tucked my hands up my cardigan sleeves, out of sight.

'It doesn't work, I soon bite through it. Anyhow, how many children are you going to have?'

'Two or three,' she replied. 'But I don't want any for a couple of years, so I'm going to have a cap fitted to make sure.'

How could wearing a cap stop you getting pregnant? I looked at her head. Mum said that men had to wear something. I supposed that was why so many men wore caps, although I never saw Dad take his up to bed. I decided to ask Lynn about it later. Ann might know.

* * * *

I hated having to do homework and look after Josie and Ian. I wanted to go out more at night with Lynn and Hazel, another friend, who met up with us more often now. Hazel was a year older than Lynn and I, and was leaving school next year. She already wore bras and had periods. Lynn and I wondered when we would start.

I also began to despise school. The lads were forever touching our backsides. If they felt the bulge of a sanitary towel on a girl, the news would be all around the schoolyard by break-time.

'Rag week, rag week,' they chanted to any girl having her period.

Every time we had a cookery lesson, the lads waited outside the school gates and grabbed whatever we had made. We would then get a ticking off from our mums for going home empty-handed, especially as the cookery lesson cost two shillings.

One particular day, after the cookery lesson, when the lads had raided our tins, Lynn and I were walking down to the Wadsley Bridge terminus for the tram. A gang of girls from Meynell road school came up to us. Lynn and I glanced at each other. We didn't like the look of this.

'Too late, girls,' we said, jokingly. 'The lads have already beaten you to it.' We banged on our empty tins. They didn't smile.

'Which one of you is Jackie Campbell?' said the one at the front, her hands by her sides, balled into fists.

I looked around, afraid. 'Me. Why?' I asked, shaking.

Suddenly, I was on the floor, kicked in the stomach and being dragged up by the hair. I screamed. Lynn tried to pull the girl off. Nothing like this had ever happened to me before and I began to cry.

'Cry baby,' shouted the girl who attacked. 'That's just a warning – there'll be more. We know where you live.'

The five of them vanished as quickly as they had appeared. Shaking and crying, I brushed the dirt off my skirt. We picked up our empty cookery tins and continued to the tram stop.

'What was all that about?' asked Lynn, her face white.

'I wish I knew, I said, and I burst out crying again.

* * * *

'I don't know why you have to have cookery lessons,' Mum said, when I came home with an empty biscuit tin.

'Surely all girls know how to cook. It's in their blood.'

'Not all of them know how, Mum.'

'Maybe…' she said, and turned from the mirror to look at me. 'What's the matter with you? You look dreadful.' She adjusted the turban she wore for work.

'I got beaten up.'

'What on earth for?' she asked, fixing her headwear, not waiting for an answer. 'Well, I hope you gave them what for.'

The pressure cooker suddenly began to hiss. I went over to the stove and turned the gas down.

'Mum. There were five of them,' I cried. 'And only me and Lynn.'

'Didn't anyone come to help?'

'No, and I've been threatened – she says she's going to do it again.' I threw myself on one of the kitchen chairs.

'Don't worry, love. Lots of people say they're going to do something and never carry it out.'

'But, Mum, what if she's there again tomorrow? Then what?' I picked up a knife from the table and turned it over.

'Don't be silly. She'll have forgotten all about it by tomorrow. Pass me my coat off the back of the door.'

I put down the knife, and got her coat.

'I'll not forget though, will I?' I shouted.

'Stop it, Jacqueline. You're blowing it all out of proportion.'

'Worst of all, I don't even know why.'

'Well, next time you see her – ask.'

'And not only that, I swallowed my bubble-gum, Mum.'

She pushed an arm down her coat sleeve.

'Will it wind round my heart?' I began to cry again. She tut-tutted and shook her head.

The door opened and Dad came in from work.

'Hello, love,' he said to Mum as he took off his cap and coat and hung them up.

'What's up with you, Jack? You look as if you've lost a shilling and found a tanner.'

'Someone set about her after school,' Mum said as she fastened her coat. 'Well, I'm off, I'll see you later.' She picked Ian up and kissed him, and shouted to Josie, who was upstairs playing with a friend.

'Well, I hope you'd the sense to hit them back.' Dad said as he closed the cellar door.

'Hit them back?' I screamed, 'you've always taught me not to fight, and now all at once I've to hit them back.' I picked up the knife and threw it into the sink, then banged the door as I ran out of the house.

* * * *

I sat on the toilet, considering going to live with Auntie Doris. Let Mum find someone else to look after Josie and Ian. Why should I have to do it?

I don't know how long I'd been sitting there, when I heard Ian scream and start to cry. I ran down the yard.

'What's happened?' I asked, taking Ian from Dad.

I took him in my arms and looked him over. Tears were running down his cheeks.

'He was running round the table and fell over his train. He's cut his knee and bumped his head on the hearth.' Dad scratched his bald head.

A large blue egg appeared on Ian's forehead, and his knee was bleeding. I felt awful. This wouldn't have happened if I hadn't been in the toilet sulking.

'You finish your tea, Dad. I'll see to him.' I placed Ian in the chair while I took the medicine box out of the cupboard. His distorted face and watering eyes watched every move I made. His arms reached out for me. I hated myself.

'I'm coming, love.' My own eyes filled with tears at his grief. 'I'm just getting something to make you better.'

'Will he be alright?' Dad asked. 'Do you want me to fetch your mother?'

'I'll see how he goes.'

Josie came downstairs with her friend, said goodbye and came over to Ian.

'What's happened? Is he poorly?'

'He's fallen down,' I replied.

She gave him a hug. He screamed again, so she screamed back at him.

'Stop it,' I shouted. 'Can't you see he's injured?'

'I only want to cuddle him.' She began to cry, and then placed her hands on hips, stared at me and screamed.

I took hold of her shoulders and shook her.

'Stop it, or I'll give you something to scream about. Anyhow, isn't it time you were getting ready for bed?'

Ian stopped crying as soon as I bent down and touched his knee. It wasn't too bad after the blood had been cleaned away. The tears and screams came again as I wiped it with a piece of lint and Dettol, then covered it with Germolene ointment. The smell of antiseptic filled the room. Placing a clean piece of lint across his knee, I wrapped a strip of old pillowcase around the wound.

'There now, you can't see it, so it doesn't hurt.'

He raised his arm up to his forehead. 'Hurts,' he sobbed. I lifted him up and cuddled him to my chest. The lump was no worse, so I smeared it with margarine, sat him on my knee and told him a story about a little boy who had fallen down and bumped his head, and the lump on his head grew and grew and grew…

He quietened down after a while, and Dad finished his tea. I noticed that Josie had not washed.

'Dad, will you nurse Ian for me please while I make sure Josie gets ready for bed? Don't let him go to sleep though.'

'I don't want to go to bed,' stamped Josie, as I took her over to the sink for a wash.

The geyser burst into life as I turned on the tap and ran some warm water. Reluctantly, she lathered the flannel with soap and washed her face and hands.

'I'm not going to bed.' She stamped her foot in annoyance, and pulled the towel out of my hands. 'I'm going to wait here till Mummy comes home.' She folded her arms across her chest.

Ian, still in Dad's arms, began to cry again, and Dad turned towards me. I looked at the clock, and my homework lying untouched on the sideboard.

* * * *

Things began to change at home, but not before I took another beating.

I began having headaches in the mornings and feeling sick. Sometimes Mum let me take a day off school and sometimes, too scared to get out of bed, I feigned sickness. Then Mum and Dad received a letter from the School Board regarding my non-attendance, lack of homework and falling asleep in class. They were requested to attend a meeting, but Mum wrote a note saying they could not go, as she would be at work at the stated time and Dad would be too tired. I gave it to the teacher.

I was called to the headmaster's office, Mr Darvill, a likeable man, tall, slim, softly-spoken, with greying hair. Only the wrongdoers feared him.

He sat behind his desk with his back to the window, the note from Mum and my attendance report in front of him.

I stood opposite him, looking out onto the playing field beyond. A six-a-side football match was in progress. Two lads out of Senior 4, thinking they were hidden, were smoking cigarettes in the bike shed.

* * * *

'Jacqueline,' he said, looking very serious. 'Are you not happy here?'

'No sir,' I lied.

He looked down at the notes on his desk. 'This tells me a different story.' His grey eyes met mine. 'What do you have to say for yourself?'

'Nothing, sir.'

There was a change in his tone. 'Nothing? It does not concern you that your absenteeism and lack of punctuality will be written on your report?'

'But sir, I have to look after my brother and sister, and my Dad's not well. Mum works in the evenings so I don't have time to do my homework.'

I looked down at my shoes. 'And I've been beaten up on my way home, twice.'

'Speak up girl, I can't hear you.'

I lifted my head and told him what had happened.

He made some notes on his pad, then stood up and rubbed his chin. 'Leave that with me, I'll look into it. Did you say Meynell Road School?'

I nodded.

'Meanwhile, Mr Popple will take you in his car to Wadsley Bridge where you can catch the tram. Wait for him in the staff car park. Do you know which car is his?' He wrote notes while he was talking. 'It's the grey Ford Prefect.'

He rubbed his chin again and stood up, turned and looked out of the window towards the bike shed. He flung the window open. The sudden change was like watching Jekyll and Hyde. 'Hey! You two, my office, now!' He barked, and banged the window shut.

* * * *

Mum left her job at Bassett's and went to work at Fletchers bakery. Instead of having "misshape" sweets every Friday, we now had "deformed" bread cakes, and sliced bread. Her hours were the same, but now she worked six till ten.

She decided to open up the front room: we were growing up and needed privacy for washing, as we still had no bathroom. We still used the old galvanised bath tub on Fridays or Saturdays, but Mum insisted we all strip-wash more often. With the help of Auntie Doris, we took Dad's old velvet horsehair, dropped-arm settee into the yard, chopped it up and stacked it by the bin. Mum replaced it with a modern, low-backed settee on stainless steel legs with two matching chairs. A low-level sideboard stood in place of the old large dresser. We had a tiled fireplace, complete with a gas fire, which looked much better than the old fireplace with its high mantelshelf.

We carried the television into the room and stood it on a wooden dinner wagon in the corner. Mum gave Dad's mantel clock and prism mantel lamps to the jumble sale, along with his gilded china statue of

St George on his horse, which was under a glass dome. I had seen Dad upset and annoyed before, but never angry like this. He and Mum rowed and didn't speak for days, but the room did look lovely when it was finished, especially because Mum allowed me time off from school to do the painting and wallpapering.

* * * *

I had a visit from the girl who'd beaten me up. A man came with her. I assumed he was her father. She apologised and said it wouldn't happen again. We shook hands and I never saw her again. I never found out why it had happened either.

Mum and Dad received a letter from the City General Hospital about Josie. She had to go there for tests. Mum suspected a heart murmur, which caused her and Dad a lot of concern.

Ian started nursery school, which meant that Mum could go to work during the day. She did, but didn't give up her evening job.

After seeing an advertisement for a cleaner in a private house in the Wadsley area, Mum, fastidious about cleanliness, started working at the big house. It wasn't long before she managed to get two more cleaning jobs through recommendations. By the end of the year, she had five houses to clean, five days a week. This meant I had to do a lot more chores around the house, and had to take time off school if Josie and Ian were ill, which didn't go down well with my new form teacher, Mrs Wilkinson. I often wished that Mum didn't go to work, even though I knew it gave us a lot of extras, and we did have more money than the girls at school whose mothers didn't work.

When I went to their houses, I noticed it more often: all the things we used to have. Their mums waiting at home with freshly made bread, cakes or buns; warm fires, music on the wireless. Now our house was cold when we came in, or Mum would be just coming in or going out, and with no time for cooking, almost everything we ate seemed to come out of a tin.

I was fourteen and fed up. Most of my friends at school were going out a lot more now they were older and only had another year of schooling to do. I always had to take Josie or Ian with me. Mum insisted that the extra money she earned was necessary. Because of Dad's age, he had to take whatever work he could get, which wasn't well paid.

'If I can't go out, can I have a dog?' I asked Mum one tea-time.

'No,' she said. 'Definitely not.'

'But why? Everybody else has one.' My bottom lip drooped.

'Stop exaggerating. How many of your friends have got one?' She was getting ready to go to her evening job.

'That's beside the point. Why can't I have one?'

'Your Dad wouldn't have one in the house, and well you know it.' She passed me some shirts. 'Here, you can sew some buttons on these if you want something to do.'

'But, Mum, Josie can do that.'

'No I can't, I've got homework to do,' Josie interrupted.

'So have I, and I can't get mine done for looking after you lot.' I stood up and shouted at her.

'Sit down.' Mum glared at me. 'Who'd look after it, eh? I'm out during the day. And you're at school.'

'I'd take it out before I went to school and when I came in,' I pleaded.

'I'll tell you what you can have. I'll get a new sewing machine and you can make some new clothes for Josie and new curtains for the front room.'

'I don't want to make Josie some new clothes – or curtains. I want a dog.'

'Yes, Mum, can we have one? Then I can play with it,' Josie said. She was eating some awful-looking pudding that had come out of a tin can and looked more like frogspawn than rice pudding.

'No you can't. It would be my dog, not yours,' I replied. She pushed out her tongue and waved the spoon at me.

I reached over the table to grab her. She suddenly jumped up and screamed as the flypaper strip dropped from the ceiling and into her dish.

I sat back down and laughed as she jumped up and down, screaming.

'Serves you right,' I said, still laughing as the sticky yellow paper covered in flies curled into her pudding.

She threw the spoon across the table. I ducked and it landed on the sideboard.

Mum stormed towards us and clipped us both on the back of the head. 'Shut up, the pair of you, there's no dog coming into this house and that's final.'

10

I went to see Auntie Doris, to see if I could live with her.

'Don't be silly, Jacqueline,' she said, with her arm around me. 'Your mum needs you at home.'

'No she doesn't. All she cares about are the precious people she cleans for.'

'Come on, love, drink your tea.' She handed me a mug of tea. Granddad coughed, just to let us know he was still with us.

'Your Mum's never had much love. She was the eldest of eight, remember? Had to go into service at fourteen. She'd only been gone a year when she had to come back – our mum died having her ninth child, and it died too. Margaret was the eldest. No more than a child herself, but she had no option other than to return from Leeds to look after us.'

'I know all that, but it doesn't make me feel any better. It's me that has to face the teachers at school over my non-attendance reports.'

'Don't go worrying about that, love. How good are you at English lessons?'

'Good, I suppose.' I looked across at Granddad, who was trying hard to light a cigarette.

'Good? You surprise me, Jacqueline. I thought you'd do better than that.'

'Very good, I suppose.'

'What did it say on your last report?' She folded her arms across her chest, and tucked an escaping green curl under her turban.

'Excellent.'

'That's better. Now, what about sums?'

'Same, excellent.' I gave a proud half-smile.

'Then you've nothing to worry about, have you?'

'Why haven't I?'

'Because, if you're good at reading and writing, and doing sums, you'll be able to work in an office or a shop.'

'So?'

'You'll not get mucky like you would if you worked in a cutlery factory – or even razor blades, surgical knives and scissors.' She lit Granddad's cigarette for him and one for herself, and then offered me one. I backed away. 'Haven't you started smoking yet?'

'No, I haven't, and won't. Mum says they're bad for you.'

'Your Mother used to smoke, you know.'

'Yes – I remember – it was at the same time I gave up my dummy. She said it would be easier for her if we did it together. Anyhow, what's wrong with working in a factory? Swann Mortons are building a new place. At least I'd have a regular supply of sharp scissors for cutting Dad and Ian's hair.'

* * * *

Lynn and I were going to the pictures one night and we needed make-up. Our mums didn't wear much, but Lynn's sister did, as she was now working.

Lynn borrowed it. She came round to our house so we could apply it, because my mum and dad didn't mind me wearing make-up. All Dad said was, 'what are you putting that muck on for?' He laughed when I added a beauty spot high up on my cheekbone.

Lynn and I borrowed Josie's paint box and painted black lines up the backs of our legs. We hoped it wouldn't rain.

The cinema was empty when we arrived, but by the time the Pathé News came on, it was half-full. The lights dimmed and the lads' eyes began searching for any empty places near where the girls were sitting. Before long, they came bounding over the seats.

'Can I sit with you, love?'

This was their chat-up line – as some lad simultaneously sat himself beside you and placed his arm around the back of your neck. We couldn't tell what they looked like in the semi-darkness. After a while, a few bubble-gum pops could be heard, perhaps a loud belch or a fart. A few giggles and laughs would follow, with the sound of seats tipping back.

'Awgh! Christ, warra stink,' annoyed people moaned as they moved to other places.

The usher came round, shining his torch.

'Pack it in you lot, or I'll have you out.'

Silence would reign for a few minutes, until he was out of sight, and we'd all move to different places, and start again.

It was best when an Elvis or Buddy Holly film was on. Lynn, Hazel and I went to see Jailhouse Rock three times. When Elvis appeared on screen and began singing 'Jailhouse Rock', it was our cue to scream and dance. More people were dancing in the aisles than sitting in seats.

* * * *

We were having a bit of gang trouble in our area. A few of the older lads, the sixteen and seventeen year olds, gathered on the street corners. They wore fingertip-length draped jackets with velvet collars, and drainpipe trousers, slightly short in length to show their fluorescent shocking-pink, lime-green or acid-yellow coloured socks. Thick crepe-soled shoes finished their outfits, which some people called brothel creepers. The lads could be quite intimidating. Some carried brass knuckle-dusters and flick-knives with blades that sprung out at the touch of a button. Some had flick-combs, which opened like a flick-knife, but a comb would spring out instead. We called them trick-knives.

The lads would pull them out of their top pocket, as if making a threat, and then would calmly comb their D.A. "duck's arse" hairstyles. They were our heroes, and we hung around them, wearing similar clothes and hairstyles. They ignored us though; we were too young, but we stayed in the background with the younger lads, watching and learning.

* * * *

The Walkley gang sometimes came to our area, and sometimes, the Parson Cross gang. They taunted us from the other side of the road. Very little traffic travelled on Penistone Road. Earlier in the day, children would wait for occasional passing cars and record their number plates on a scrap of paper.

The rival gangs would play-fight loudly, pushing each other into the road, getting nearer to our side, but never crossing the invisible line. Our lads would be watching and doing similar things. Threatening glances, swapping flick-knives, flick combing, gum chewing, depositing a few globs of spit into the road, and after a while, everyone would go home.

* * * *

One night, a new lad appeared. He wasn't with a gang. He stood alone, not too tall but quite stocky. Some other lads followed him, keeping a few paces behind. Our lads quietened at this intrusion and stopped talking. In the distance, I could see the Parson Cross gang coming over the hill in the opposite direction. They stopped and stared.

The stranger didn't stay on the other side of the road. He walked straight across it, and up to our gang.

'Anyone here want to take me on?' he called, raising his fists, taking a step forward.

'You?' He pushed a fist into the shoulder of the nearest lad, Irwin Peak.

Irwin stepped back. The stranger did the same to Trevor Clarke.

'What about you?' he asked, taking another step forward. 'Who's your best fist?'

He looked at them all in turn.

The lads stopped chewing gum and glanced at each other, heads and eyes slightly lowered. The Parson Cross gang kept their distance.

'Nah, just havin' a few laughs,' Leyton, the gang leader mumbled, with lowered eyes. He stepped back and grinned at the others, who were standing with hands in pockets, thumbs hanging out, looking downwards, as they shuffled their crepe soles in the ground.

'Not laughing at me, are you?' The stranger pushed him in the chest.

Leyton moved back and looked over at us, his jaw working rapidly on the gum.

'Nah, just chattin' up the birds.'

We stopped popping our gum and swinging around the lamppost as the stranger turned towards us. The Parson Cross gang had vanished.

'They're only kids.' The stranger laughed and turned back to face the lads. He spat on the floor in front of them.

'Here, you three?' We were shaking. He came towards us. 'Any of these toss-pots bother you, come and see me.' He looked back at them and spat again, then turned back to us.

'Forrest's the name, Dan Forrest. Got that?'

* * * *

'You've not been out dressed like that, have you?' Mum said when she came in from work. She took off her white overall and turban and hung them on the back of the door.

'Why? Since when have you cared how I look?'

'You look common. Have you looked in the mirror recently?'

I walked slowly over to the mirror, singing 'Be Bop a Lula.' I turned round a few times, blew a bubble, let it pop and continued singing.

'Ignore her, she's gone bloody daft. It makes you wonder what they're teaching 'em up at that school,' Dad said, scratching the blood blisters on his head.

Mum looked at me in disgust.

'Go and get changed,' she said, and then looked at Dad. 'Do you want any supper, Charlie?' She took a fresh loaf from her bag.

'I'll have a bit o' bread and cheese if you don't mind, love.'

'Have Josie and Ian been alright?' she asked Dad.

How dare she!

'How would he know? It's me who looks after 'em when you're not here. When are you going to think about what I want?' I screamed at her. 'I can't do this, I can't do that, I can't have a dog. All I'm wanted for is to do this and do that. Make some clothes for Josie, make some curtains, take Ian with me…'

I burst into tears. 'Nobody cares about me, only Auntie Doris.' I rushed to the door, slammed it behind me and ran upstairs, shouting, 'I'm going to live with Auntie Doris.'

* * * *

It was shortly after this incident that Lynn and I started drinking and smoking. Mrs Lingard was an old widow who lived on her own next door to Lynn. She paid Ann, Lynn's older sister, to fetch a couple of gills of beer from the beer-off for her every night. As Ann was now working and going out most evenings, the task had become Lynn's.

'Two gills of bitter please,' said Lynn as she handed over the tall white jug. 'Mrs Lingard says to make them gudd'uns,' Lynn added.

'She always gets a good measure from me,' said Tom, his huge arm pulling hard on the pump.

There were four beer pumps on the counter: two for bitter, one for mild and one for stout. The shelves behind the counter were full of bottled beers and Tizer, made in the factory across the road from his shop. He handed over the jug and Lynn gave him the coins.

'There's not much in here,' said Lynn, looking at the contents and then at Tom.

'Be off wi' you, the's more than a good measure in there, and don't ye go suppin' it on't way 'ome.' He handed the change to Lynn.

We walked along Penistone Road, turned down Beulah and then on to Lynn's. It was dark in the entry so we both had a drink from the jug.

'Ughh! Don't know what they see in this, do you?'

'It's not a bit like Tizer, is it?'

'Nor Dandelion and Burdock.'

'Here, let's have another taste.'

'I don't suppose it's too bad when you get used to it.'

'My Dad would call it an acquired taste,' I said, laughing. I raised my little finger as I took another drink from the jug.

'Do you think we'll get drunk?' Lynn wondered. She staggered, laughing, down the entry as she went from wall to wall.

We looked in the jug; it had gone down by half.

'Hold on to it,' said Lynn, and passed me the jug. 'I'll just see if my dad's in.'

She opened the back door, looked around, then beckoned me to come in. We could hear voices in the other room.

'Shhh.' She placed a finger to her lips and reached towards me for the jug.

I crept over to the sink where she was standing. Placing the jug beneath the tap, she topped it up with water.

'Come on, let's go, quick.'

We made our way to the door and closed it quietly behind us, then stood outside, giggling.

'It's only me, Mrs Lingard,' Lynn said as she knocked on the door and entered. I followed.

'Ahh! There you are. I thought you'd got lost,' said Mrs Lingard, rising from her chair, glass in hand, waiting.

Lynn poured some of the liquid into the glass and placed the jug on the table.

We stood watching. She took a drink, which left a moustache on her top lip.

106

'I'm sure he's watering his ale down,' she said, as she took a drink and wiped the back of her hand across her mouth. 'Still, it's not your fault.' She looked at Lynn, who handed her the change.

'Here, I suppose you'd better have one too,' she said as she handed us both a penny.

'Thanks, Mrs Lingard. See you tomorrow,' we chorused.

'Aye, mayhap, and don't make a habit o' two of you going, I'm not made o' money.'

* * * *

We were in the old men's hut in the park. The lads had been smoking a month now.

'Here, try a drag,' said Roy, handing us his Domino cigarette.

'What do we do?' Lynn asked, passing the cigarette back.

'Watch.' He took a deep drag on the cigarette. The end glowed red. Smoke coiled around his mouth and disappeared into his lungs. Then he blew it out through his mouth and down his nose.

'Okay, let's have a go,' said Lynn, holding out her hand.

She repeated Roy's actions and began coughing, then passed the cigarette to me.

'Not likely – I can cough enough without that.'

'Wimp, wimp, wimp,' they began chanting.

I took the cigarette from Lynn, who had taken another drag and this time, didn't cough.

'It's not bad when you get used to it.' She looked across and nodded. 'Go on, have a drag. It won't kill you.'

They all bent double with laughter as my face turned green. I thought I was choking.

I gave it back to her.

'Here, try this one, it's not as hot as that one,' Walt said, and passed me one he had only just lit. I tried again, and took a few more drags before getting used to it.

We all sat on the bench seat, smoking, sharing two cigarettes between six of us. I sat at the end, with Walt next to me.

Walt was quieter than the others. I found him attractive, with his dark brown eyes and slicked-back mid-brown hair, pulled forward at the front to form a quiff. His teeth were white and straight, which was unusual, as many of the lads had crooked or missing teeth.

The lads tried to decide on which was the best brand of cigarettes. Most of them agreed on Dominos and Park Drive, as they were the cheapest. Others said Senior Service and Player's Navy Cut were good, but more expensive. The best by far was Capstan Full Strength, but not many shops stocked them.

'My Dad's pipe tobacco isn't bad if you're desperate,' said Malc, Custard to his mates. They all laughed.

'You've never smoked that, 'ave you, Custard?' Dave Hunston asked.

'Yes – got some Rizla-papers – look.' He felt in his trouser pocket and pulled out a small, orange-coloured packet. He took out one of the fine paper strips and showed it us. I wondered how they could possibly know so much about cigarettes. After all, they had only been smoking a few weeks.

Some scruffy kids rode by on their pushbikes. They turned their heads and looked at us.

'Dirty wankers!' they called, and circled the hut. We looked at each other and laughed. They rode by again.

'Jam rags!' shouted one, lifting both hands off the handlebars and steering with his knees. They circled again, full of bravado.

'Tits!' shouted a small boy, leaning forward, his head down, trying to outrace the older riders.

Dave Hunston and Custard, being nearest the entrance, shot out after them and threw their tab-ends at them. The kids stood up on their bikes, and pressed down on their pedals to make a quick getaway.

Walt and I stayed seated, looked at each and laughed, which turned to a smile as our eyes met, and then we just stared. It felt as if we had seen each other for the first time. I suddenly felt Walt's arm slide around the back of my neck.

11

Wednesday was outdoor physical training at school. I hated it. I hated all sports, especially rounders. It meant standing out on the field, freezing cold, in a short-sleeved shirt and long navy-blue shorts. We didn't have our own kits: they were communal and kept in a large wicker basket in the gym. If you were late for school, you had to take whatever was left. Last time, I'd worn a size forty shirt, even though my chest was only thirty inches. And shorts so big and baggy, they had to be fastened with nappy pins to hold them up. I could get my whole body inside one leg. It didn't stop there. How could you run in plimsolls that were either two left feet or two rights, or a left and a right in different sizes?

I walked up the street, dreading it. Mum had refused to write me an excuse note. A sudden squeal of brakes startled me, as Mrs Brown's dog ran straight out from the entry and into the road. The lorry driver cursed and Mr Ford, another neighbour, shouted at the driver. I met Lynn at the top of the street.

'What was all that about?'

'It's the lorries. They drive too fast. Mum says they'll be hitting a child one of these days.' I walked a few paces with Lynn and then stopped. 'I'm not going today, Lynn, it's P.T.'

We decided to wag it and go to the park instead. We sat in the old men's hut, and talked about how much we hated school and couldn't wait to leave. One of the park keepers came past and stopped.

'Shouldn't you two be at school?'

'We've got dentist appointments,' I replied. 'What time is it?'

'Nearly ten,' he replied.

'Come on, Lynn, we'll be late. Thanks, Parky.' We started walking towards the Hillsborough entrance.

'Now what?' Lynn asked, stuffing her hands in her pockets.

'We'll look in the shops down Hillsborough.'

'What if our mums are shopping?'

'We'll have to make sure they don't see us. My mum won't see us. She's working till dinner time. Come on, stop being so miserable. We can go in the Sarsaparilla bar –'

'But we've no money.'

'We can use our tram fare and dinner money. That'll get us a drink and some cigs.'

'You're not old enough, they'll not serve you.'

'We can try, come on.'

We went in the first shop, a newsagent.

'A packet of Dominos, please,' I said, holding out a shilling.

'How many?'

'I don't know. How many's in a packet?'

'Two, four…'ere, you're not old enough to buy cigarettes. Bugger off.'

We carried on walking through Hillsborough and came to another shop, where a woman was standing outside with a pram, holding a screaming baby in her arms.

'This'll do,' I said. 'Wait here.'

I rushed into the shop and up to the counter. 'A packet of four Dominoes, please.' I held out the shilling. 'They're for me mum.' I turned and pointed at the woman tending the baby.

'Sounds like he's got a bit of colic,' the woman behind the counter said.

'Yes, we've been giving him Nurse Harvey's but it doesn't seem to be working.'

She handed over the cigarettes and sixpence change.

'Tell her to try Dinnefords, it worked on mine when they had it.'

'I will, thanks, bye.'

We went to the Sarsaparilla shop, bought a drink of Vimto, and sat on the high stools, listening to Danny and the Juniors singing 'At the Hop' on the juke box. We danced together. I took the lead as I was taller. Lynn swirled round and round as I spun her beneath my raised arm. Jack, the owner, watched from behind the counter and nodded his head to the beat. A few people came in so we sat down. No one put any money in, so we decided to leave.

'Come on, Lynn, let's go up to the meadows and have a fag. See you later, alligator,' we shouted to Jack as we left.

'In a while, crocodile,' he replied, grinning.

* * * *

The sun was high in the sky. We sat on the gravestones, looking out over the river Don, watching the smoke pouring from the steelworks' chimneys. The smell of sugar wafted up from Bassett's.

'Do you think we'll get a sun-tan?' Lynn asked, removing her cardigan, showing her pale pink arms.

'More likely soot freckles,' I said, as the smoke from the chimneys suddenly turned our way. We lay back on Martha Louise Bentley's slab. 'Dad's first wife is buried somewhere up here,' I said.

'Did your dad have any kids with her?' Lynn asked.

'No. They never happened. He laughs about it, says he went all those years without any and then when he reaches his sixties, he's got three.'

We watched the clouds, like overhead pillows in the smoky blue sky.

'Do you think you'll ever move away from here, Jack?' asked Lynn.

I thought for a moment.

'Where to? Everywhere's the same, isn't it?'

'I'm not sure. I don't think other areas are as mucky as this.'

'Well it's not smoky when we go to Cleethorpes on the club trips, is it?'

'Can you imagine what it would be like living there?'

'You'll have to find a rich man who can take you in his car.'

'Yes, and live happily ever after, like film stars.' We burst out laughing, and then lay back with thoughts of marriage and children whirling in our heads.

'Your Walt put his arm around me the other day.'

'When? I didn't see that.' She sat up.

'When we were in the old men's hut, smoking, and those cheeky kids came round on their bikes.'

'I never noticed,' Lynn replied. 'Where's the cigs?'

I sat up, reached in my cardigan pocket, and took out the packet of cigarettes. We both put one between our lips while I reached for a match. I'd taken a couple out of Dad's box that morning and put them in my pocket. I struck it on the gravestone and cupped my hand round it while Lynn took a drag and lit up. I lit mine and flicked the match into the brush.

Whoosh! We jumped up. The dried grass caught alight. Stamping our feet, we tried to put out the rapidly spreading blaze. Lynn grabbed her cardigan and began wafting the flames, which only made it worse. The flames got higher and quickly all the dry scrub around us was alight.

How could it spread so fast?

'Run!' we screamed at each other, searching for a way through.

'Over there. Make for the white bridge.' We ran, but the flames were faster. In seconds, the hillside behind us was ablaze and the fire was creeping towards us.

We stumbled through nettles, our feet and legs tangled in brambles. Tripping over rubbish, we finally made it to the other side of the bridge. With white faces, shaking with fear and hearts thumping in our chests, we looked back at the fire burning out of control. It had spread all the way to Herries road.

'Oh hell, what have we done?'

'You barmy buggers,' a man walking his dog said to us. We started to cry.

'Cry as much as you want, I've sent for t' police. And I know where you live,' he added.

Another wave of fear rushed through my veins.

We started running again, keeping a lookout for the coppers. Then we stopped, not sure which way was best.

'Hold on a minute. We're on the other side of the river, so it can't spread over here,' I said to Lynn, who wiped some blood off her leg with her hankie. 'And that man. He couldn't have told the police – he's miles away from a phone box.'

'But he said he knew where we lived. I'm too scared to go home, Jackie. My dad'll kill me.' Lynn began crying again.

'So will mine.' More fear ran through me. My stomach was like a rollercoaster. Sweat poured down my face, yet my teeth were chattering.

'Come on, let's go down to the river and get cleaned up a bit.'

'No, we'd better get well clear of here, just in case that bloke did tell the police.'

'We can't go home looking like this. They'll know something's wrong.'

Lynn suddenly had an idea. 'Let's go to Mrs Lingard's – we can clean up there. I'll ask her if she wants a cup of tea making, then we can have one.'

'Good idea, it's only three o'clock. School won't have finished.'

We fast walked, exchanging glances and taking quick looks behind us as we made it to the main road.

'Is it that time already?' Mrs Lingard said, as Lynn knocked on the door, entered and offered to make a pot of tea.

'No, we've finished early today. We thought we'd call and see how you were.' Lynn lit the gas and put the kettle on to boil.

Mrs Lingard returned to her rocking chair. 'Well, that's very considerate of you, Ann,' she said as she sat down.

'I'm Lynn – Ann's working now,' shouted Lynn.

We sat in silence with our thoughts for what seemed like hours, while Mrs Lingard drank her tea, rambled on about her ailments and then fell asleep. We cleaned ourselves up as best we could, then the clock chimed four, making us both jump.

'It must be tea-time,' Mrs Lingard said, as she rose from her chair. 'I'd better put the kettle on; do you two want a cup?'

'No thanks, Mrs Lingard, we've just had one,' Lynn said, looking at our full cups.

'Well you could have made me one, Ann. Your Lynn does when she calls in.'

Any other time, we would have thought it funny, but today was different.

Mrs Lingard made her way to the stove and lifted her head into the air. 'Can you smell something burning?'

We closed our eyes and gulped, then ran out of the house and down the entry, straight into Lynn's sister.

'What are you doing here?' she asked.

'Just been to see how Mrs Lingard is,' replied Lynn, trying to sound calm.

'Oh,' she replied. 'Have you seen the meadows? They're on fire.'

* * * *

'What on earth have you done?' Mum asked when I got home.

I gasped. *She knows.* I began to cry.

'I'm sorry, Mum. I don't know how it happened.' Shame and fear overwhelmed me. I don't know which was worse, setting the meadows on fire or Mum finding out I'd been smoking.

'Let's have a look at those legs.' She pointed to the chair for me to sit down, and went to the cupboard for the medicine box. She took out some cotton wool and the bottle of Dettol.

'Have you seen the meadows on fire?' Mum asked as she dabbed the cuts.

I stopped shaking and looked up. She didn't know.

'Where did this happen?' She smeared Germolene over the scratches.

'Err, on the way home from school. Some lads were chasing us.'

'Well, it's a good job you were nowhere near that fire.' She put the box back in the cupboard, and washed her hands.

'I'll have to get ready for work. Can you sort something out for your tea?'

'I'm not hungry, Mum.'

'I'm not surprised. Look at the state of those nails. I wish you'd stop biting them, love.'

Then Dad walked in.

Frozen to the spot, I waited for the axe to fall. Did he know?

'That's some fire, eh!' he said, as he hung up his cap and coat and looked over at me. 'What's the matter with you? You look as if you've lost a shilling and found a tanner.' He looked at Mum, who was putting on her overall. 'What's happened?'

'She's had a bit of a fall, that's all.'

I ran upstairs, worrying what time the police would arrive.

'Teenagers!' I heard Mum say.

* * * *

Lynn and I went with Hazel into town on Saturday morning. We told her about the fire. She said it could be seen from Walkley, where she lived.

Hazel said there was some nice black skirt material on the market. We bought a yard each, and seven-inch zips, and then we went into the meat and fish market where we bought cockles and mussels, covered them in vinegar and ate them off small plates. And we couldn't go into town without visiting Woolworths. The make-up counter was a must. We studied the models in magazine adverts, and copied their makeup, deciding that we would look exactly like them when we left school. Then went home and made our skirts.

No pattern was needed. Wrapping the material around our hips, a pin was placed where we needed to sew. The excess fabric was removed and the selvedge made a waistband. We sewed zips in the back seam, front and back darts for our narrow waists, and press-studs to fasten the waistbands. We tried them on, and decided on length, cut the spare fabric off and turned up the hem, leaving a six inch split up the back. The new sewing machine Mum had bought certainly made a difference in sewing time.

* * * *

Mum said my skirt looked good, and that I could borrow her bat-wing blouse with the butterfly collar to wear with it tonight. We were going to the flicks to see *The Blob*, which had an "A" certificate, meaning that under-sixteens had to have an accompanying adult. Standing outside the Phoenix cinema waiting for some likely persons, we asked a young married couple.

'Can you take two in, please?' We held out our hands with the money. Once inside, we moved away from the couple and sat near the back with other teenagers who had also managed to gain admittance. Walt and the lads appeared shortly afterwards. A thrill ran through me as they climbed over the seats when they saw us.

'Can I sit next to you, Jackie?' Walt asked, sat down and placed his arm around my neck. Terry sat with Lynn. The Pathé news came on screen with its usual fanfare. The Queen re-opened the new Gatwick airport, Comet jets were going to fly the Atlantic and Britain was to have parking meters.

Who cared about the Queen? Only the ones who stood up at the end of the films to listen to the National Anthem, then tut-tutted as we pushed past them to leave. And when were any of us ever going to own a car or fly in an aeroplane? I did listen to the part where it said Donald Campbell had set a new water speed record. Only because we shared the same surname and I could tell everyone he was my uncle.

I moved my head back and rested it on Walt's arm. It felt nice. I pouted my lips. After all, I was Jane Russell. We watched the adverts and the trailers for future films, and finally *The Blob* began. After a slow start, the film became exciting. Our eyes were fixed on the screen as the great red blob made its way through towns, eating everything in its path, getting larger by the minute as it spilled across the screen and down every High Street. It became even more thrilling when it went into the back of the cinema and devoured the projectionist, poured through the projectionist's windows, headed towards the viewers sitting in the balcony seats and then spilled over the balcony.

Realising we were in a cinema, we looked behind us. We turned back towards the front as the people on screen shouted and screamed. We watched their futile attempts of escape, as they tried to outrun the approaching Blob, which wrapped itself around their feet in the semi-darkness and drew them in. It was hard to tell where the noise was coming from. Was it from the cinema on screen or from inside our cinema?

The noise above us in the balcony became louder, and we heard the sound of stampeding feet. Something was wrong.

Lynn and I looked at each other. Walt and Terry moved their arms. We jumped up and began to run. Others in the cinema stood up and started rushing towards the exits. What was happening? Viewers near the front screamed and jumped up as water from the balcony poured onto their heads.

The house lights came on and the film stopped. We ran outside and regrouped, only to find out that Dan Forrest had been on the balcony and had tipped a couple of fire buckets full of water over the front edge.

We didn't go back to the flicks – we went to the pie shop instead. We joined the queue, still laughing and talking about *The Blob* incident. Jim Pickles was at the front.

Dan Forrest came in. He walked straight to the front, looked around and then at Pickles. Without taking his eyes off him, he picked up a bottle of Henderson's Relish from the counter and emptied it over Jim's head. Jim just stood there, glaring, and turning bright red.

'Sorry fat twat, I thought you were a pie,' said Dan.

* * * *

Dan, supposedly banned, caused so many problems at the Phoenix cinema that they gave him a job as an usher. He quietened us down much better than the usual usher, made sure we behaved, and stopped the lads from climbing over the seats. He wasn't really such a spoilsport. He opened the emergency fire doors in the toilets to let us in without paying.

'Don't all go through at once,' he said.

* * * *

Later that year, Lynn and I wanted see the film *Dracula* but it had an "X" certificate, and we were underage. Auntie Doris told us to wear make-up and a headscarf, and to make sure we carried a large purse. I wondered why women carried such large purses when most of the time, they were empty.

She said to clutch our purses close to our chests with one hand while we paid. I couldn't see how this would work, but it did. We did exactly as Auntie Doris said and handed the payment over to the cashier; cigarettes hanging from our mouths, purses clutched. We passed for sixteen-year-olds.

The film was terrifying. We watched through finger-covered eyes as Dracula came alive at night, forced the women onto beds, and instead of kissing like in other films, he bit them on the neck and turned them into vampires; not just women but men as well. We left the flicks in a state of shock, vowing never to let any boys near us, in case they were vampires.

It seemed extra quiet when we left the cinema and everyone went their separate ways. We were filled with false bravado as we made our way through the dark lanes, past the old church, taking another way home, hoping we wouldn't see any of the lads. We parted company at the top of Lynn's street. It was Wednesday and the fish and chip shop was closed, making the area extra quiet. When I arrived at the top of the street, I stopped dead. The lamp at the bottom was out. I daren't go down. Everything I had seen in the film was now very real.

I walked halfway down and stopped. It was dark. I went back to the top and waited. I thought that someone might come along who was going down the street and I would be able to walk down with him or her.

No one came.

My hands and feet were freezing. Thankfully, a policeman came by and asked if I was alright and why I was hanging around.

I couldn't tell him I'd been to the flicks to see *Dracula*.

'I'm waiting for my mum to come home,' I said, trying to smile.

'Why, where is she?'

'She works at Fletchers, the bakery,' I gulped.

'What time does she finish?' He looked at his watch.

'Ten,' I mumbled.

'She should be home by now, it's half past.'

'Is it?' I said, trying to sound amazed. 'I'd better be off then.'

'Okay, I'll watch you down the street.'

Thank goodness for that, I thought. He is going to walk me home.

He didn't. He just stood and watched as I walked down the middle of the road, keeping well away from the entries.

I daren't look back, and I daren't go down. I was halfway down the street when a figure came out of our entry. I jumped.

'There you are. Come on,' she shouted. 'What time do you call this?'

'Mum!' I shouted. 'Wait –' but she turned and went.

I glanced up the street. The policeman had gone too. I still didn't dare to go down the entry. I decided to wait for Mum to come and look for me again.

She didn't.

It was pitch black. The entry was a dark menacing hole with vampires at the end. I took a step nearer and looked down the passageway. Count Dracula, waiting, his cape flapping, or was it a dustbin and a sheet on a washing line? Could I outrun him? No, he could turn into a bat and still get me.

I stood for a moment biting my fingernails. *Mum, where are you?* I suddenly thought of my silver cross. In the film, a crucifix was a deterrent. If it was held close to Count Dracula, he crumbled and turned into dust. I clutched my throat. My necklace. It wasn't there. I stifled a scream. It had been a present from Mum and Dad. I remembered that the chain had snapped and had not been repaired.

I had to make a run for it, even though I would be turned into a vampire. I closed my eyes, swallowed hard, covered my throat with my hand and ran down the entry.

A figure in a white gown moved slowly up the yard.

I screamed and dashed for our door. It opened.

'What the 'devil's the matter?' asked Dad, as I fell into him.

'It's a ghost, I've just seen a ghost.' I was shaking.

Dad looked out. 'Don't talk bloody daft.'

I peered out from the safety of the house.

'It was there, going up the yard. Look! It's there.'

'Silly bugger' he said. 'It's old Tom Bates going to the lav.'

'But what's he wearing a nightgown for?'

'It isn't a nightgown, it's a night shirt.'

12

Lynn and I decided we were not going to see any more "X" films until we were old enough. Meanwhile, we had to protect ourselves. I sewed together the broken links in my chain with cotton thread and began to wear it.

'Mum, have we any garlic?' Mum was only half listening. She had received a letter from the hospital saying an appointment had been made for Josie to see a consultant regarding her suspected heart problems.

'What did you say, love?'

'I said have we any garlic?'

'Garlic? What's garlic when it's at home?'

'I just wondered.' I went round to Lynn's. Her mum didn't know either.

'Let's ask Mr Green at the fruit and veg shop. He'll know.'

'Garlic? Never get asked for it,' Mr Green said. 'New-fangled recipes coming out all the time though.'

'But is there anything similar?' We waited while he took a pinch of snuff and stuffed it up each nostril.

'I suppose it depends what you want it for.' He sneezed a few times, then wiped his nose with a brown hanky. 'Ahh, that's better,' he said, sniffing.

Lynn and I glanced at each other.

'Don't know. Mum asked me to get some.'

He gave us a strange look and scratched his head.

'I think it belongs to the onion family.'

'Do you think that would do?' I whispered to Lynn.

We looked at the sack of onions. 'They're a bit big,' Lynn said.

'What about Spring Onions?' Mr Green lifted up a bunch to show us.

'What do you think, Lynn?' She nodded.

We took out our purses. 'How much is that bunch, Mr Green?'

'Here, take it. Bring me some newspapers next time you come in.' He shook his head, laughing.

* * * *

It was Saturday, and Lynn was staying overnight. Mum and Dad were watching the Black and White Minstrels on TV and Josie was playing school with Ian.

'I'll not be late back, Mum,' I called as we left.

The lads were waiting for us at the top of the street.

'Where are we off to then?' Lynn asked, blowing a gum bubble in Terry's face.

'Dunno. Has anyone any money?'

The lads looked in their pockets and Lynn and I took out our tiny purses.

'Three and seven between us. That'll not get us to the flicks,' Custard said.

'It's a pity Forrest got the sack – he would have let us in,' Dave replied, scuffing his shoes on the pavement.

'Come on, let's walk over the meadows – it's light enough tonight,' said Walt. Our eyes met. I felt myself blushing. I turned around and looked up at the sky. It was an autumn moon, with just a few odd clouds passing.

Dave went into the shop for a bottle of pop and some cigs.

Walking around the back of the dog track, we stopped and looked in through the broken fence.

'Pity we 'aven't got a rabbit to throw over. That would put the cat amongst the pigeons.'

The lads all laughed and barked as the dogs ran around the track.

We made our way to the white bridge over the river, and up the hillside where we sat on the gravestones.

All traces of the fire were now gone. Looking out, we could see the lights of the stadium. Thursday was the best day, when the speedway was on. The heat and roar of the engines as the riders lined up; the sweet smell of Castrol R, as the bikes raced around the track. Tonight was quiet. We sat and smoked our cigarettes and talked about leaving school next year.

A large cloud passed over the moon, and Walt came and sat by my side. Even in the darkness, I knew it was him; he always smelled of Palmolive soap. He put his arm around me.

'Do you mind?' he asked.

I felt myself blushing again. I leaned against him.

'What are you going to do when you leave school?'

'I don't know. Lynn and I are thinking of going to night school to learn shorthand and typing. How about you?'

'Engineering, I'll probably get taken on at Easterbrook and Allcard's. Dad works there, so he'll get me an apprenticeship.

I shivered slightly. Walt moved closer.

I turned my face to his.

'Thanks –'

His lips were on mine. A tingle ran through me and I closed my eyes, like they did in the films. At that moment, I wasn't Jane Russell, or Liz Taylor. I was Jackie Campbell, and I was in Walt's arms, being kissed. There was no one else on the planet.

We separated, and looked at each other in the semi-darkness. It was as if someone had cast a magic spell over us. His arms were still around me, and I placed my head on his shoulder. I had never been held like this, and I didn't want this feeling to go away. Nor the night to end, and I didn't want to go home.

Our moment of bliss was short-lived.

'Custard! You dirty sod,' said Roy, as Custard moved away laughing, leaving the stink behind. 'Phew! You dirty bugger.'

We all stood up and moved out of the way. Walt and I held hands as we walked together towards home in a dreamy silence.

* * * *

As Lynn was staying over, the lads left us at the top of our street.

'Don't forget what we've got to do tonight,' said Lynn as we neared our entry.

'No, I'll get the candle and scarves when I get in.'

We held hands and ran down the entry together. There was no Count Dracula, or Tom Bates going to the toilet this time.

'Hello, Mr Campbell,' said Lynn, as Dad nodded. He lit his pipe and went through to the front room, leaving a trail of smoke behind him.

'Charlie,' snapped Mum, wafting the smoke away, and continued placing some cheese on a slice of brown bread. 'Do you two want a sandwich?'

'None for me, thanks.' I went over to the pantry and took a white household candle off the shelf.

'No thanks, Mrs Campbell,' Lynn replied.

'Can I borrow this, Mum?' I picked one of her brass candlesticks off the top of the fireplace.

She looked puzzled on seeing the candle in my other hand.

'Yes, but don't go setting the house on fire.'

I took two of Mum's sheerest headscarves out of the sideboard drawer and nodded to Lynn.

'We're off then. Goodnight Mum.' I kissed her on the cheek and opened the door to the staircase. 'Goodnight Dad,' I shouted, as Lynn and I climbed the stairs.

'You can smell those onions,' said Lynn as we climbed the second set, up to the attic.

I placed the candlestick and candle on the dressing table. I'd already threaded the onions together on a piece of string and draped them around the mirror.

124

'We'd better get undressed,' I said.

We slipped off our clothes and donned our pyjamas.

'Are you scared?'

'No,' I lied. We stood barefoot and looked into the mirror. Our pale faces looked back. 'I'll light the candle.'

I felt in my windcheater pocket for a match, and struck it on the base of the candlestick. An eerie glow filled the room as I turned off the light. Shadows danced over the walls as I moved back towards Lynn and the dressing table.

'Are you ready?' I asked, as we both picked up a scarf.

'Yes…' Lynn hesitated. 'Aren't we supposed to be wearing nighties?'

'Yes! But we don't wear nighties now. Pyjamas will have to do.'

We looked at each other and picked up the scarves.

'Wait, I can't see your crucifix.'

Lynn unfastened the top buttons of her pyjama jacket.

'That's better,' I said, as the silver cross glistened in the dip of her throat.

I adjusted mine so it could be seen in the mirror.

We looked at each other.

'Ready?'

Lynn nodded. We picked up the scarves.

'On the count of three, one, two…'

'What if it doesn't work?'

'Lynn!' I snapped. 'What now?'

The candle flickered as I lowered the scarf.

'It might not, because we're not wearing nighties.'

'Lynn. Pick up the scarf.' I snatched it off the dressing table and thrust it into her hand. 'Now, when you're ready, we're going to close our eyes. Place the scarves over our heads, count to thirteen, and then open them. Then, over our left shoulder we'll see an image of our future husbands.' I raised my scarf above my head.

'But what if we see Dracula?'

'We won't, we're wearing our crucifixes and we have onions

around the mirror. Now concentrate.' We stood for a moment. 'One, two…'

Suddenly the skylight rattled and the candle went out. I dived over to the light switch, tripped over my shoes, stubbed my toe and switched on the light. We looked around and jumped into bed.

'Are you two alright up there?' Mum's voice came up the stairs. 'We've come to bed now, goodnight.'

13

Mum took Josie to see the consultant. When she came home, she told Dad and me that the tests had discovered that Josie had an enlarged heart and a small hole.

'Nothing can be done yet,' Mum said. 'She's still growing. They can only operate when she reaches the age of sixteen.'

'Will she be alright?' I asked.

'She has to live a normal a life as possible, but she mustn't over-exert herself. No playing field sports, and if she gets tired in the day, she'll have to rest.'

Josie was oblivious to our conversation, her head buried deep in a book. Mum went on to say that Josie would require regular monitoring. The consultant would send a letter when her next appointment was due.

In the days and weeks that followed, we all watched over Josie. Mum and Dad were worrying as if she might drop down dead at any time.

Even I, who had stopped saying my prayers at night when I moved into the attic, began saying them again. Josie had also recently had her TB vaccine, and her upper arm was sore and full of pus.

On Saturday, I took Josie and Ian into town so they could spend their pocket money. Women hurried with shopping bags over their arms. Curlers in their hair were partially covered with hairnets and large headscarves, in readiness for the coming evening's events.

We shuffled around Woolworth's, carried along with the crowd. The floor creaked with the weight and movement. Knowing how busy it would be, I hadn't brought Ian's pushchair. He was on reins and his vision was restricted to feet and legs.

I kept lifting him up to look at the toys on the counters, glad that Josie was almost as tall as me.

We went to the outdoor Rag and Tag market to watch the pot man selling his tea and dinner sets. The different sets, displayed in large wicker laundry baskets, were stacked on a bench. The pot man stood on a platform and threw the baskets, full of cups, saucers and plates to his brother at the other end of the stall. Equally skilled, he presented them to the increasing crowd of onlookers, and then threw them back to his brother.

He tapped a cup and saucer together.

'Listen to that, genuine bone china.' He passed a few of the pieces to the crowd, for them to examine. Standing near the front, I watched, fascinated by how the men handled the pots. Mum would have a fit if we threw our pots around as the two men were doing.

A woman standing by my side, called out. 'Have you any pudding basins, Joe?'

'No, love. I'm at Stafford next week. I'll 'ave some nice ones when I get back – blue and white stripes, in sets of three.'

'Thanks, Joe, I'll see you next week.' She pushed back through the growing crowd.

He raised and replaced his cap, picked his cigarette off the edge of the bench, took a few quick drags and carried on with his patter.

'This genuine bone china tea-set in Walsh's or Cockaynes, up the road, would cost at least twenty quid. But I'm not going to ask anything like twenty quid,' he shouted and banged on the bench with his gavel, making the tea sets rattle and clink. 'I'm not even going to ask half of that. I'll tell you what I'm going to do.' Hesitating, he looked under the counter, and came back up, holding some more pots.

'Look here, come closer, the's plenty of room…' The crowd gathered closer and I was hemmed in. I switched Ian over to my other arm, wishing I had brought his pram. Josie, holding the shopping bag, was leaning against me. A woman standing nearby saw me.

'Here, love. Do you want to rest him on here?' She made room on her pram. Her baby, about a year old, was sucking on a Farley's Rusk.

Still holding onto Ian, I sat him on the edge.

'Thanks ever so much,' I said. 'He's getting a bit heavy.'

'Take your time, get comfortable,' said the pot man. 'Would you like an easy-chair?' he added, jokingly showing his annoyance. The crowd laughed. He lifted and dropped his cap again, then reached for his cigarette which had burnt away on the bench. He lit another one while the crowd settled.

'Right, where were we?' He looked over the bench. 'Ahh, yes. What we have now is an eighteen-piece tea set, a matching teapot, with a milk jug and sugar bowl.' He added the extras to the basket and banged on the bench with the gavel. 'Twenty-one pieces, yes, you heard correct, twenty-one pieces. But I'm not asking twenty quid for this twenty-one piece fine bone china tea set. Just a minute. Listen, I'm gonna tell you summat – listen to this.'

He leaned forward, making eye contact with each section of the crowd.

'I was selling on Barnsley market the other day, and a woman bought an identical set for ten pounds. Do you know what she was going to do with it?' The crowd hushed. 'Well, I'll tell you. She was saving it for when the Queen came to Barnsley, in case she was thirsty and called in.'

He straightened back up, nodding his head.

'It's true, I tell you. That woman knew quality when she saw it.' He banged the gavel on the bench. 'Who else'll pay ten pounds?'

Some of the crowd shuffled and put their hands in their pockets. He banged the gavel again. 'Hold yer horses.'

The crowd grew still.

'I'd sooner come here than Barnsley, so I'm going to give you a treat. You'll not get a better deal in the whole of Yorkshire.' He adjusted his cap again.

'In fact, I'll make you a promise. If you can get the same set as this any cheaper, I'll give you another set, free.' The crowd gasped. The man who had moved next to me said to his wife.

'Of course you can't get the same set anywhere else. It wouldn't be the same set then.'

The woman looked at him, bewildered.

The gavel banged on the bench. 'Listen.' The crowd quietened. 'Just as a matter of interest, who's getting married?'

A few people raised their hands.

'Who knows someone who's getting married?' Even more people raised their hands.

He tapped the basket with the gavel. 'Perfect wedding present, eh?' He looked back at the crowd. 'Now listen carefully.' He leaned forward and tilted his cap. 'Listen, because some of you are going to be disappointed.' The gavel banged as he straightened up.

'I have only three sets left,' he shouted and looked across at his brother at the other end. 'Is that right, Fred, three sets?' His brother raised three fingers in the air and nodded.

'Three sets.' His eyes scanned the waiting crowd. 'Wait for it,' he shouted, and pushed his cap to the back of his head. 'I'm not even asking ten quid, not even nine, eight or seven.' The gavel came down. 'First three hands showing a fiver – gets 'em.' The gavel banged again and fell to the platform.

Fast movement and shuffling erupted from the crowd as it surged forward. We were pushed against the bench. At least ten arms and hands reached up in the air waving the thin white paper notes as if they were winning raffle tickets. I couldn't see how many were behind me.

Four lads appeared from nowhere with ready packed tea sets, while the seller collected the fivers, and reached under the table.

'Well, what luck,' he said, as he reappeared. 'I've just found some more, and another one.' He passed the sets up to his helpers. 'Oh, an' here's another. It must be your lucky day, love…mine too, I've just found another.'

14

It was the Sunday after we had just put the clocks back an hour.

Auntie Doris came to tell us that Granddad had died during the night. She sobbed into her hanky and wanted Mum to help with the laying out. After the recent *Dracula* incident, I hoped I didn't have to help. Luckily, Mum said I had to stay home and see to things, as she didn't know what time she would be back. The following day, she went with Auntie Doris into town to get the death certificate.

* * * *

Granddad's funeral was on Friday 6th November 1959.

I had just turned fifteen and would be leaving school at Christmas. I didn't have anything suitable to wear to the funeral.

Mum borrowed a black mac from a woman she worked with. It was far too big, but she said I could turn it up, providing I unpicked the hem before it was returned to its owner. With large stitches, I turned the hem and sleeves up about six inches, and then polished my black school shoes.

Dad said he would join us after work and Audrey said she would see to Josie and Ian. Mum and I walked up the hill to Granddad's council house. All the curtains were closed. Aunties and uncles were gathered in the living room and kitchen. Auntie Doris and Brenda were busy making endless cups of tea. They burst into tears as each group of new people arrived, hugging each other and sniffing into handkerchiefs. We went over to join them.

'Your hair looks nice, Auntie Doris,' I said, admiring her blonde curls. This wasn't one of her usual do-it-yourself jobs. There were no green or orange ringlets.

'Thank you, Jacqueline. Madge Marsden's done it. I got something for you when I was there – I'll give it you after the funeral. Have you been in to see your Granddad yet?' She handed me a cup of tea.

'No. Not yet.' I hadn't seen a real dead person before and didn't want to, not after seeing Christopher Lee and Peter Cushing in *Dracula*. Lynn and I hadn't had a good night's sleep since. I listened to the conversations and drank my tea.

Mum took hold of my arm and steered me towards the front room. I pulled back.

'I haven't drunk my tea yet.'

Mum took my empty cup and placed it in the sink.

'I don't want to look,' I said, pulling away from her.

'Don't be silly, Jacqueline. What's there to be afraid of?'

Stakes through the heart, vampires, dead people jumping out of coffins. I didn't tell her any of this. She would have had a fit knowing I'd been to see an X-rated film, not particularly for sneaking into see it, but for the after-effects it was having on me.

'I don't know. Nothing, I suppose.' I hoped she couldn't see my guilt.

'Did Granddad ever hurt you when he was alive? No. Well he's not going to hurt you now, is he?' she said, not waiting for an answer. 'It's the living you've to be afraid of in this world, not the dead.'

She steered me into the front room, which was lit by the central light bulb and whatever light came through the curtains drawn over the bay window. People were looking into the coffin and wiping their eyes. I lowered mine as I neared and looked down at my shoes. Coldness crept over me and a strange smell filled my nose.

I'd never smelled garlic, so it might have been that. Mum nudged me in the back.

I slowly lifted my head and peered through squinty eyes until I could see Granddad. The inside of the coffin was nothing like the

132

ones in the film: they were satin lined. Granddad's coffin was just plain wood, with a small pillow for his head. My eyes adjusted to the artificial light as I opened them fully.

Granddad was wearing a threadbare suit that was miles too big for him. I suppose it must have fitted him at some time. His shirt collar had been turned and put back on the wrong way. I couldn't see if there were any bite marks on his neck. I couldn't see any garlic either. His face looked puffy and sallow. If it hadn't been for the hollow of his missing eye I wouldn't have recognised him.

How did Mum and Auntie Doris manage to straighten him? I'd only ever seen him bent double, even when he was sat in his chair. I looked at the strange small grey-blue markings on his face. I'd never noticed them before.

'Shrapnel,' said a man's voice, as if reading my thoughts. I looked up at the man standing beside me, steadying himself with a shaky hand on his walking stick. He had similar markings on his face, and was staring down at Granddad. 'We were at the Somme together. We were the lucky ones.'

He took a handkerchief out of his pocket, wiped his eyes and blew his nose. 'The war's over for him now,' he added and limped away.

I looked at Granddad's gnarled hands, and his nicotine-stained fingers and looked down at mine to see if they were stained yet.

Mum gently stroked Granddad's forehead. Then, leaning forward, she kissed him. I almost found it strange that he didn't move.

'Goodbye, Dad,' she mumbled and placed her hands on his. Her tears fell onto his face. She dabbed at them with her handkerchief. I stepped back, hoping I didn't have to kiss him.

'It's time.'

Two men wearing black suits came into the room. The crowd of people slowly dispersed. Standing in the doorway, I watched as they fastened the top onto the coffin. Uncle Jack, Uncle Eric, Uncle George and one of the men in black carried the coffin out to the hearse and slid it into the back. Wreathes were placed on top.

One of the men drove the car, which slowly made its way up the hill to the church. The other man led the procession as we all walked behind. The people who couldn't walk up to the church said their farewells and made their way home. The smell of last night's fireworks and bonfires hung in the frosty air.

We congregated inside the church, which was as cold as the world outside.

'Stop it,' said Mum, as I stamped my frozen feet.

The vicar said a prayer and talked about Granddad's life. I was dozing off when an awful wailing sound filled the church. I jumped up full of fear, as the organ erupted into life and everyone stood up. What's happening, where were we going?

'There is a green hill far away…' The vicar began singing. The congregation joined in. I had never heard anything so terrible in my life. Dad had some cheek to tell me that my Johnny and the Hurricanes records were terrible. No one deserved this racket for their send-off.

After the service, they carried Granddad's coffin into the graveyard and lowered it into the ground. We all picked up a clump of earth and threw it onto the coffin. The clump I picked up had a metal trouser button in it, but I threw it anyway. Mum pulled me towards her; held me close. He's got a spare button now, I thought.

* * * *

Afterwards, the funeral party congregated in Granddad's favourite pub, all rubbing their hands and stamping their feet in the warmth of the Park Hotel. The women removed their black headscarves and coats as the heat penetrated their frozen limbs.

'Go to a funeral in November, and yours may be next,' said Uncle George as he stood in front of the fireplace.

'Shut up and shift your fat arse, George,' said Auntie Doris as she pushed him out of the way. 'You make a better door than a fireguard.'

She moved to where he had been standing. I hoped she wasn't going to do her party piece and lift her skirt to warm her brains.

The landlady handed round copper trays from the bar, filled with

134

potted meat and corned beef sandwiches, along with chunks of black pudding. Slices of date loaf and black bun followed. Granddad's family and friends drank to his departure, and to absent friends. Even Mum, who never drank anything alcoholic, had a small sherry.

'What is it you've got for me?' I asked Auntie Doris, who was ordering drinks at the bar.

'I'll tell you later. Here, take these over to our Jack and Betty.' The cigarette dangled from her bottom lip as she handed me the bottles of Mackeson and Guinness.

'Does your mother want another sherry?' she asked, as I returned and picked up the glasses. I turned and looked across the smoke-filled room at Mum's face. Her eyes were puffy and her cheeks were red, but then, so were most people's in the room.

'No. I don't think so. But I'll have one.' I waited for her reaction.

Auntie Doris grinned. 'And a sweet sherry please,' she shouted to the barman. 'Here, don't let your mother see you drinking it.'

'Don't suppose you've got a spare cigarette as well, have you?'

Auntie Doris's eyes widened.

'Ooh, get you!' She felt in her pocket, pulled out her cigs and matches and placed them on the bar. 'Thanks, Alf,' she said to the barman as she put the change in her purse, then looked at me and nodded her head towards the glass of sherry and cigarettes.

I drank the sherry in one gulp and took a match, and a cigarette out of the packet, and slipped them into my pocket.

'How much did the Co-op insurance pay out, Doris?' Auntie Pat asked when I went over to their table.

I slid the cigarettes and matches across to Auntie Doris. 'You left these on the bar.'

'Thanks, Jacqueline.' She winked at me. 'Twelve pounds eighteen shillings,' she said to Auntie Pat. 'And the Pearl insurance paid out six pound ten. Which was better than I thought, as he only took it out in 'fifty two. Whereas the B & C one, he took out when our Jacqueline was born in forty four.'

Auntie Pat took a sip of stout, giving her an instant moustache.

135

'Did you get the divi as well?'

'Of course. That's the best thing about getting everything at the Co-op, the divi.'

I went to the toilet and lit the cigarette, but it was too cold outside. I went back inside and stood in the lobby.

'Ey up, Jacqueline, you've grown since I last saw you. Hardly recognised you,' said Uncle Eric as he passed by. 'Have you left school yet?'

I still had the cigarette in my hand.

'Nearly,' I replied, taking a drag on the cig and blowing the smoke up into the air. 'Might be seeing you soon – thinking of coming to your place for a job. Mum says there's plenty of money in scrap.'

'Ey, I only work at Bramall's I don't own it. Got to dash – goin' to see our kid's father,' he laughed.

A draught of cold air blew in as the outer door swung shut. I finished the cigarette, dropped it on the floor and crushed it underfoot.

'Pack up your troubles in your old kit bag' greeted my ears as I returned. Auntie Vera was playing the piano, and the family and friends were singing one of Granddad's favourite songs. Later, Auntie Doris and Auntie Mary lifted their skirt hems as they stood up and sang 'Knees up Mother Brown'.

The afternoon wore on and into the evening. Dad joined us after work. Auntie Doris passed him a bottle of Guinness and some sandwiches she had saved.

'How'd it go, love?' he asked, as he took hold of Mum's hand. She took a sip of her sherry, removed a hanky from up her cardigan sleeve, and dabbed her nose.

'Grand. He had a good turnout, as you'd expect. He's at peace now.'
He's at peace now? What was she talking about? The war finished years ago.

The evening finished with the singing of 'We'll meet again', creating more tears and damp hankies. We fastened our coats, left the smoke-filled pub, and went out into the smog-filled night. Everyone coughed, some spat.

'It's not the cough that carries you off, it's the coffin they carry you

136

off in,' Uncle Jack said, as he slapped those who were coughing on their backs.

Shivering in the cold, damp air, we hugged and kissed each other, then went our separate ways.

I walked home arm-in-arm with Mum and Dad, wondering what Auntie Doris had bought me. I also wondered if Granddad had ever played cricket, and why he'd never mentioned it. He must have been a decent player in his past, because everyone said he'd had a good innings.

15

All the curtains were open the next day when I went back to Auntie Doris's to help her tidy up. Her eyes were like Mum's, still red and puffy. We sat and had a cigarette – one of hers, and a mug of tea. She had been sorting out Granddad's clothes. As no one pegged rugs any more, no one wanted his old clothes.

'Looks like they'll have to go to the rag-man when he comes round,' she said, putting the clothes in a pile. 'I hope he's got some donkey-stone instead of goldfish – last one didn't last two days. Mind you, I didn't have a jam jar big enough.'

'What did you get me?' I asked.

She went over to the cupboard and took out a brown bottle.

'Here, Jacqueline. This is what you need for your hair.'

I frowned as I looked at the label: Hydrogen Peroxide 10 volume. 'What's it for?'

'Your hair – you said you'd like to be more blonde like your friend, so this'll do it.'

She unscrewed the top and pushed the bottle under my nose.

'Phew! That stinks.' I pushed her hand out of the way.

'Sit still and I'll show you how to use it.'

'It'll not end up like yours, will it?' I pulled away from her, afraid of the consequences, Mum's words of old coming back to me: *Don't always believe what our Doris tells you.*

'Sit back down. Of course it won't. Your hair's not permed like mine.'

She took a small piece of cotton wool and poured a little of the liquid onto it. Taking hold of a few strands of hair above my forehead, she wiped the pad over it, and then repeated it a few times around the front and sides of my hair.

'We'll have another cig while we're waiting,' she said and opened the packet. The ends of her fingers had turned white. 'Has your Mum changed her mind about you having a dog yet?'

We lit the cigarettes.

'No, she won't hear of it. It's not fair – Josie can have everything she wants. Why do you ask?'

'Farm up't road, Mr Marshall. His collie's just had pups.'

My eyes lit up. 'Sheepdogs – black and white ones?'

'Hmm.' She picked up the comb and poked its tail into my hair. 'We'll give it five more minutes.' The ash fell off the end of her cigarette, into my lap, as she spoke. 'Have you got a boyfriend yet, Jacqueline?'

I felt myself blushing. Why the sudden change of subject? I wanted to know more about the collies.

'Sort of. They call him Walt. He lives in the next street. We've been out together a few times now. Mum wants to meet him.'

'Ooh! It's serious, then?' she grinned.

'No, of course it isn't.' I looked away and a thrill ran through me as I thought of Walt and his dark brown eyes.

'Your Mum's right, Jacqueline. We don't agree on everything, your Mum and me, but she just wants to know who you're knocking about with.'

'Auntie Doris, about these collies…'

'Come on, let's get you over to the sink,' she interrupted.

We pressed our spent cigs in a saucer on the table and moved over to the sink.

The geyser fired up and shook as she turned the knob, and held her hand beneath it.

'That's okay, bend over.' She pushed my head beneath the water and rubbed the front and sides of my hair. After a few minutes, she turned the geyser off and handed me a towel. I rubbed my hair and looked in the mirror. 'There, that's better,' she said.

I turned my head from side to side and looked at my reflection. The front of my hair was blonde, with tiny bleached streaks down the sides.

'It's so hip,' I said. 'Thanks.' I gave her a big hug.

'It'll look even lighter when it dries,' she replied, looking quite chuffed.

* * * *

Mum disapproved. She said I was naturally dark and should not change it. It went down well with my school friends though. Even Lynn had a go with the peroxide, which lightened her sandy blonde hair. For Lynn, there was no going back. She would be blonde for ever more. It made a difference at school too. Boys who had never bothered with us before suddenly started taking an interest.

Lynn was staying over again, and we lay in bed talking about the effect our new hair colour was having on some of the lads.

'Did you notice how Barry Bishop and John Breedon's filling out?' Lynn asked.

'Yes, and they've grown taller too.'

'I thought you were into Terry?'

'Naw, we're just mucking about. Not like you and our Walt.'

'I know. I'm in love.'

'Dig you.' She turned onto her side to face me.

'Does his name suit me? Jackie Mcreath?'

'It's not much different to Campbell.'

'Mrs Mcreath. It's got a certain ring to it.'

'Not like Camp-bell.' Lynn laughed. 'Does our Walt feel the same?'

'I think so. He's carved our initials in a heart on a bench in the old men's hut. He's gentle and not at all groping like some of the lads when we go to the flicks. And when he kisses me, I imagine it's like being kissed by Elvis.'

'Does he put his tongue in your mouth?'

'No. Why would he do that?' I turned to face her.

'Our Ann says that's proper kissing.'

'Walt's not kissed me like that. I'd make him stop if he did. Mind you, we've swapped bubble gum and spearmint, and that was alright.'

* * * *

I took down the hem and sleeves of the borrowed mac, and returned it to its owner.

'Thanks for the loan of the mac, Joan,' I said as I hung it on the back of the door.

'Anytime, Jacqueline,' Joan replied.

'I hope not. I don't want to go to any more funerals, thanks.'

Joan laughed. 'Not pleasant, are they?' she said.

'The booze up after wasn't bad, though.' I grinned as I opened the door.

'Well you know what they say. Laugh at a funeral, cry at a wedding.'

'Is that so? Well, thanks again.'

'Hold on a minute, Jacqueline.' She put down the iron. 'Your Mum says you do the decorating at your house. Would you mind doing my kitchen? If you do a good a job, you can do the rest of the rooms.'

I didn't know what to say. 'I'm not sure…'

'I'll pay you – I don't expect you to do it for nothing.' She took a packet of Park Drive cigarettes off the top of the fireplace and offered me one.

'Thanks.' I took one out of the packet, and we lit up.

'I don't like painting – it's too slow, but I'll do your wallpapering if you'll cut the edges off the rolls.'

'I'll get my eldest lad to do that. Okay, ten shillings for the walls, and ten for the ceiling.'

I couldn't believe my ears, and pictured the green paper notes. I

141

looked around at the walls and ceiling. They were more bellied than ours, but nothing I couldn't handle.

'Is your plaster sound?'

'I've no idea. How can you tell?'

'Pass me your long handled sweeping brush.'

Holding it by the head, I raised the handle and gently tapped the ceiling – I didn't want it falling down, and then knocked it against the bulges in the walls. I handed back the brush.

'They're not bad. When do you want me to start?'

'Well, that's up to you. It's got to fit in with school, hasn't it?'

'Nah. I've nearly finished anyhow.'

* * * *

It was Saturday, and two weeks before Christmas. We were all at home. Mum and I were doing the usual cleaning. She was upstairs, I was downstairs, and Dad was in the front room, reading the morning paper. Josie was decorating the Christmas tree and Ian was playing with his toy cars, when Auntie Doris arrived.

'Can't hear t'kettle boiling,' she said as she came in, and went straight over to the stove, lifted the kettle to see if there was any water in, and lit the gas.

I got the cups out of the cupboard and put them on the table. 'Mum,' I shouted. 'Auntie Doris's here.'

'Down in a minute,' she shouted back.

'Close your eyes, Jacqueline, and hold out your hands.' She reached into the shopping bag hanging over her arm.

What's this all about, I thought, some more stuff for my hair? I did as she said.

She placed something warm and fluffy in my hands. I opened my eyes and looked. A lump came in my throat as a small pink tongue licked my fingers.

'Auntie Doris,' was all I could say. I cuddled it to my chest. 'It's beautiful. Is it for me?' My eyes filled with tears as Auntie Doris

142

looked at me, smiled and wrinkled her nose.

'What are you going to call him?' She went to the stove and made the tea.

I had to sit down. I was overwhelmed. I looked at Auntie Doris as she poured the tea into the cups, and the small furry pup nestled on my lap. I cried, I was so happy.

'Ahh, how sweet,' said Mum, as she came into the kitchen. 'Whose is it?' She looked at Auntie Doris. The smile disappeared.

Auntie Doris didn't look at Mum as she put the cups on the table. 'That's yours, Margaret.' She pointed to the green spotted one. 'I'll just take one to Charlie.' She quickly slid past Mum.

'Please let me keep it, Mum. Look how he loves me.'

She looked on as the pup nestled down into my lap.

'No, your dad'll have a fit.'

'But Mum.' I held the pup towards her. Her eyes softened as the pup gave a tiny yawn, and looked at Mum with his dark blue eyes.

'You'd better go and ask him.'

I jumped up.

'Honest, Mum, can I keep him?' I was so thrilled and ran into the front room where Auntie Doris was talking to Dad.

'Dad, look what Auntie Doris has brought me.' Auntie Doris's eyes widened, and she stepped back out of the way.

'What the –?' said Dad as I placed the pup in his lap.

'Can I keep him, Dad? Please?'

The pup licked Dad's hand. Dad didn't know what to say as the tiny creature looked up at him and yawned, showing the tiniest of teeth, then closed his eyes and curled himself into a ball on Dad's lap.

'Ahh, whose is it? Can I hold him?' said Josie, followed by Ian. Their eyes were wide open.

Dad began to stroke him.

'He's mine,' I said, jubilant. 'He's called Shep and the best Christmas present ever.'

* * * *

Lynn and I were now in the same class and there were only a few weeks to go before leaving school.

One morning, after assembling in class, we opened our desk lids. Each row of pupils looked across and grinned at each other while hidden from the teacher's view. We banged the lids down all at the same time.

'Stand up!' he barked. 'Now sit down and do it again, QUIETLY.'

We repeated the exercise, silently, apart from Roy Turton, whose lid crashed down as it slid from his fingers. A blackboard rubber flew past his head and landed on the floor. Mr Newman stormed past him, cuffed him on the ear and clouted Pete Atkinson who sat opposite him grinning.

'That's for laughing,' the teacher said.

Pete Atkinson rubbed his ear. Mr Newman picked up the rubber and walked back to the blackboard. Roy's face and ear glowed red.

Mr Newman suddenly turned and stared at me.

'Ah! Jacqueline, I see you've decided to honour us with your presence.'

I quietly took out my pen and pencil.

He came towards me and held out his hand.

'Homework?'

'Sorry Sir, I've –'

'What's the excuse this time? Spontaneous combustion? Vaporisation?'

The class burst out laughing and banged their desk lids.

'QUIET!' Mr Newman glared.

He pressed his fists on my desk and pushed his face towards mine.

'Is that what happened to it?' He looked around at the rest of the class. 'Or did some aliens steal it to see how the human brain worked?' He straightened up and looked back at me. 'You'll stay in after school and do it then.'

'But sir –'

'No excuses.' He walked away.

144

* * * *

'I thought we were going to sign up for night school?' Lynn said at break-time.

'We still can. I told Mum where we were going and that I'd be home late.'

'What about your homework?'

'What homework?' I laughed, as the bell rang for end of break.

The official enrolment date for night school had been in August and September, but Lynn and I hadn't bothered then. A notice had recently been posted on the school community board stating that places were still available.

We returned to our classroom.

Later, just before lunch, we were reading a poem. Lynn sat at her desk making notes in her exercise book. Sitting at the desk behind her was David Hunston. Crouching so the teacher couldn't see him, he took a matchbox out of his pocket and removed a big green caterpillar. The pupils sitting nearby could see what was happening and raised their desk lids to hide their titters. As Lynn sat back after finishing her notes, David grinned, leaned forward and dropped it down the back of her blouse.

Shortly afterwards, the teacher rapped on David's desk.

'You have just read 'The Way through the Woods' by Rudyard Kipling. What message do you think the poet is trying to convey?'

A few of us raised our hands. Lynn sat up and raised her arm, felt something move, then raised her other one behind her back and scratched. She lowered both arms as she looked over her shoulder, and then stood up. A large green stain appeared on her blouse, between her shoulder blades.

David couldn't hold it back. He burst out laughing, but soon stopped as Lynn reached forward, pulled back her arm and punched him in the face.

The school bell saved the day and we broke for lunch. Lynn went to the washrooms, removed her blouse and cleaned it up as best she could. David went to the lads' washrooms to dab his nose with cold water up to stop it bleeding. I went to the toilet and found I had started my periods.

* * * *

I had to see Miss Cooke, as she was responsible for sanitary towels.

'Is it your first, Jacqueline?' she asked as she went into the store cupboard, and asked if I needed a belt.

'Yes,' I replied.

She came out after a few minutes.

'There don't seem to be any belts, Jacqueline. Can you manage with a piece of string?'

I took it with the towel to the toilet. It was more like rope than string as I threaded it through the loops and fastened it around my waist. It was so uncomfortable.

I went back to see Miss Cooke during the afternoon break and told her how the string was making me sore and cutting into my flesh. I asked if I could go home.

'Yes, you'd better if it's that bad,' she replied.

'Thank you, Miss. Will you explain to Mr Newman why I can't stay behind tonight?'

* * * *

On Monday evening, Lynn and I attended our first lesson for shorthand and typing. The session was held in the top section of our old school on Parkside Road.

We were sitting in class facing the windows, trying to absorb the peculiarities of the shorthand symbols, which the teacher was trying to explain. We were bored, as she droned on about Sir Isaac Pitman and how he had introduced this method of speed writing in 1837. We couldn't even see into the park as the windows were too high.

Suddenly, there was a dull thud on the window. Everyone looked up and the teacher turned around.

'Must have been a bird,' she said, and returned to her lecture.

Shortly afterwards, there was another thud. Annoyed, the teacher stood on her chair to look out, but she was still about a foot too short. A small clump of earth with grass attached to it slid down the outside of the window.

'Ignore it, and concentrate on the lesson,' she said, as she stepped off the chair.

Lynn and I looked at each and grinned. We looked down at our shorthand notepads, trying to ignore the distractions. We glanced up and in the bottom windowpanes, we could see hands waving, and then Custard and Dave Hunston's faces appeared in the window.

They were grinning and pulling faces, precariously balanced on some other lads' shoulders. We couldn't help but laugh, and so did others in the class. The teacher stormed out of the room. That was the beginning and end of our shorthand lessons, and for me, the end of schooling altogether.

16

I was more than happy training Shep. On one of the tins of dog meat was a label inviting you to register your new pup with Spillers and they would send you some sample foods.

We had to keep a record of what the puppy liked and disliked, and then send the record card back to Spillers. A small parcel arrived shortly afterwards with a colourful booklet telling you how to look after your new puppy.

'He's got to have inoculations for certain illnesses,' I said to Mum.

'I'm not going that far, Jacqueline. Letting you keep the dog is one thing, but paying for vaccines is another matter. Vets aren't cheap.'

'Never mind,' I said to Shep. 'I'll make sure no harm comes to you.' I cuddled him to me.

* * * *

I officially left school on the 16th of December 1959. I didn't attend the official leaving day, and my school leaving report came to me by post a few days later.

ATTENDANCE: Poor.

PUNCTUALITY: Fair.

The words stood out like chapel hat pegs.

'How do you expect to get a job with a report like that?' Mum threw it onto the table.

'But Mum, you knew I was taking time off school to go wallpapering...'

148

'Not as much as it states here,' she snapped.

'You weren't complaining when I handed over the money, were you?'

She glared at me. 'You've never gone without.'

'Turn the pages, Mum. The work reports are good, look!'

She scanned through the pages. 'Perhaps so, but who's going to bother when they see the first page?'

'I'll tell them to look past the first page and explain the attendance and punctuality thing.'

A look of annoyance crossed her face. 'What? You're going to tell them you took time out from school to earn money for make-up and cigarettes?'

I flinched. 'What cigarettes?'

'Don't give me that. I know you've been smoking. I can smell it on your breath, and I've seen the fag-ends thrown from the attic window.'

I looked away. 'Well, you used to smoke!'

'Yes, before I learned any sense. I'm surprised at you, what with your chest.'

'That's a laugh – it doesn't make much difference living here surrounded by all this smoke and Dad's pipe, does it?'

A knock on the door interrupted us, and then it opened. Shep ran towards the door, giving a little yap.

'What's this, then?' said the window cleaner, as he bent down to fuss Shep. 'Can I have some clean water, please?' Shep was climbing all over him.

I took the bucket from him and placed it in the sink.

'Got to have clean windows for Christmas, eh, love?' he said, as he stood up and waited in the doorway. He lit a cigarette and Shep ran back under the table as the match struck. 'Have you been down to the new Castle Market yet?' He put the spent match back in the box.

'No,' Mum replied. 'Have you?'

'I haven't but the Missus has, says it's all right. They've still got the rag and tag outside though.'

I handed him the bucket of water.

'Thanks, love. I'll just finish this cig and move on.'

'Here, I might as well pay you now,' said Mum, reaching in the drawer for her purse. 'Save you coming back later.'

* * * *

The row Mum and I'd had earlier was forgotten and we went shopping. While she was in the post office collecting the family allowance, I looked at the adverts on postcards in the window.

'What about this Mum?' I said when she came out. 'Young shop assistant required for busy chemist, Dykes Hall Road, experience not essential, will train. It's got a phone number to ring.'

'Well, are you going to ring it, or stand there looking at it? There's a phone box across the road.'

'No, I'm going to go, now, and if they ask for my school leaving report, I'll say I've only just seen the ad and didn't want to miss my chance, but I'll run and fetch it if necessary.'

'You've got it all worked out, haven't you? Here, let me have a look at you.' She took a step back. 'Where's your comb?'

I felt in my black patent bucket bag, gave my hair a quick comb-through, and re-applied my Shocking Pink lipstick. I looked at my reflection in the window.

'That'll have to do. What do you think, Mum?'

'Turn around.' She knocked some fluff off the back of my coat. 'Go on then, good luck.'

A bell tinkled as I opened the door. The smell of perfume and cosmetics filled my nose. I closed the door behind me and the bell tinkled again. Nearing the counter, camphor and menthol added to the heady mix.

An assistant was serving a gentleman. She was wearing a long-sleeved coral-pink nylon overall with banded cuffs. The stiff fabric rustled as she reached up to a shelf for a bottle of Milk of Magnesia, and I noticed brass-rimmed vent holes in the under-arms. She

150

finished serving, and placed the money in the till.

'Can I help you?' she asked, turning towards me.'

'I've come about the vacancy,' I replied.

'Have you phoned? It's usually by appointment.' She tidied away some paper bags on the counter.

A feeling of disappointment ran through me. 'I was down Hillsborough when I saw the advertisement and came straight away. I didn't want to miss my chance.' I stood, unmoving.

'Just a minute, I'll tell Mr Fox. What's your name?'

My mood lifted. 'Miss Campbell. Jacqueline.'

She nodded, smiled and went into the back of the shop. I looked around. The shop was crammed full of stock. One area held baby products, small tins and jars of Heinz and Gerber baby foods.

The assistant came to the front of the shop, carrying a cardboard box. 'I've told him you're here,' she said and began placing bottles of Nurse Harvey's and Dinnefords on a shelf in the baby area. Ostermilk 1 and 2 were placed on lower shelves.

I looked to her left, where straight and crescent-shaped glass feeding bottles glistened in the light, along with tins of Johnson's baby powder and glass tubs of zinc and castor oil cream. I didn't realise how many different baby products there were. A hanging card held packets of nappy pins, pink and blue dummies and bottle teats.

I watched as she continued filling the shelves, humming away to herself until the box was empty and then returned to the back of the shop. Another area with floor-to-ceiling shelves was stacked with health foods: jars of calf's foot jelly and Slippery Elm Food and Malt, which Mum had made us have when we were younger. There were bottles of Virol and Sanatogen tonic wine.

Smaller items of non-prescription medicines and remedies such as Blaud's Pills, Beecham's pills, Carnation corn plasters, Anusol pile ointment and Vicks Vaporub were aligned neatly in pigeonholes at the back of the counter.

At the front of the shop was a large glass cabinet, full of cosmetics containing Coty and Max factor make-up, Yardley's Bond Street

Perfume and dusting powder. A large glossy card advertising Cutex nail polish pictured a lady's hand with long slender fingers, wearing bright red nail polish. I wished my hands and nails looked like that. There was an extravagant midnight-blue and silver display promoting Evening in Paris perfume, with a tester. I loved it. I wanted to touch it all. The bell tinkled again and a woman came in carrying a baby.

'Hello,' she said. 'Are you being served?' She removed the outer shawl from the baby.

'No,' I replied. 'I'm waiting to see Mr Fox. I've come about the job.' I looked at the baby, with his big blue eyes peering out from beneath his knitted blue helmet. 'He's lovely. What's his name?'

'Paul,' she said, her eyes gleaming with pride, as she removed his hat. 'There now. Are you going to smile for the lady?' She cooed to him and then looked at me.

Lady? She called me a lady. 'Can I hold him, please?'

An anxious look crossed her face.

'Make sure you support his head,' she said, as she handed him over.

I held him in one arm with his head nestled in the crook of my elbow, and tickled his tummy with my other hand. 'How old is he?'

'Six months on Sunday.' Her unease vanished as he began to gurgle, wave his arms and kick out his legs. 'I can see you're used to handling little ones,' she said, and smiled again.

'Yes, I have to look after my baby brother and sister.' I turned as the assistant came into the front of the shop.

'Mr Fox won't be long, Jacqueline – he's just finishing a prescription,' she said. She went over to the woman. 'Hello Mrs Clayton. Have you brought Paul to be weighed?'

'I have, and myself,' she replied, removing her coat. 'Shall I get weighed first while this young lady is holding Paul?'

She glanced towards me. 'Do you mind?'

'No, not at all,' I replied. 'I could take him home with me.' He chuckled as I tickled his tummy again.

'You'll soon bring him back when he starts crying for his food.'

The woman laughed as she slipped her shoes off and stepped onto the scale.

Rocking the baby, I watched as the assistant slid the brass weights along the bar.

'Nine stone six, Mrs Clayton.'

'Good, that's another two pounds I've lost.' She stepped back into her shoes.

'Yes, you're doing really well.' The assistant slid the weights back to zero, entered Mrs Clayton's weight on her record card and lifted an infant scale onto another counter. Placing a clean nappy in the basket, she took the baby from me. He began to cry as I handed him over.

'He's took to you, hasn't he?' said Mrs Clayton, as she fastened her coat.

'Thirteen pounds seven ounces,' said the assistant as she handed Paul back to his mother and entered the weight on his card.

I heard a noise and turned as a small, chubby, elderly-looking man appeared from behind the counter. He lit a cigarette and then spoke, quite fast, and posh. Mum would have said he was dapper.

'Miss Campbell, hello. Would you like to come through?'

'Er yes, of course.' I looked back. 'Goodbye, Paul, Mrs Clayton.'

'Good luck,' she said.

Going towards the back, I saw high on a shelf at the back of the window, three very large, fancy-shaped bottles filled with different coloured liquids, red, blue and green. They looked so colourful, even in the pale winter sun.

'What's in the large bottles up there?' I pointed to the bright colours.

He didn't look up.

'Carboys? Swan neck carboys. Chemical mixtures, mainly iodine for the red, copper sulphate for the blue and nickel sulphate for the green, plus other additives to ensure they don't fade.' A cigarette dangled from his mouth as he spoke.

I had no idea what he was talking about. I'd never learned

anything like that when I was at school, or had it been taught when I wasn't there?

He pointed the way into a poky little office.

'Sit down, please. It is Jacqueline, isn't it?' he asked, peering over his glasses and relighting the cigarette, which had gone out.

'Yes,' I said, as I sat on the only chair in the office. The office was so small, there wasn't room for two. There wasn't even a door. I sat on the edge of the chair, feeling nervous and wishing I had gone home and put my make-up on properly before coming. The phone suddenly rang and I jumped.

'Excuse me, please,' he said, as he reached behind me to answer it.

I moved out of the way while he took the call. The desk was overflowing with delivery and packing notes, unopened mail and pharmaceutical magazines.

I glanced at last night's edition of the Sheffield Star, opened on the crossword page, two words short of completion. Invoices were poking out of black ring binders on shelves above my head, and a calendar with the dates crossed off, advertising Andrews Liver Salts, was pinned to the shelf edge with a drawing pin

The office had clear glass windows and I could see into the dispensary. Cupboards, drawers and shelves lined the walls, reaching from floor to ceiling. Freestanding metal shelves held large bottles of pills, tablets and capsules. Large jars and tubs of ointments were placed on the lower shelves, along with the largest bottles I'd ever seen, full of different coloured liquids. In another area, rows of clean empty medicine bottles and jars sparkled, ready for filling. There were so many different ones.

My eyes roamed everywhere. I felt as if I was in Aladdin's cave. Mixing bowls, pestles and mortars were in another area, along with small marble slabs with palette knives.

I took a deep breath. I wanted this job more than anything else. My stomach turned as I thought of my leaving report in the sideboard drawer back home. *Please don't ask for it.* I looked back at Mr Fox.

'Sorry about that.' He replaced the phone and picked up a note pad. 'Can I have your address please?'

He wrote it down, commented that I was local, and then asked my age, and which school I attended.

I noticed his nails were bitten down to the quick, and I curled my fingers into my palms.

'Fifteen,' I replied. 'I used to go to Chaucer, but I left last week, so I could start straight away, if necessary.'

'What marks do you have in your subjects?' He spoke with the cigarette between his lips, one of his feet resting on the rail of the chair I was sitting on.

Here we go, I thought. 'Excellent and Very Good marks in all English and Maths subjects, especially spelling and algebra. Excellent marks in Art, Craft and Needlework. Good in History and Geography, P.E. –'

'Never mind that, what grade were you in?'

'A. I've always been in the top five, apart from this year, when I dropped a grade owing to family problems.'

'Hmm!' He stroked his chin. 'How many scholars in your form?' A large piece of ash fell down the front of his white smock.

I had to think. Scholars? Form? What words were these?

'There were thirty-two pupils in our class, with a total of a hundred and fifty across the five grades,' I replied.

'What about attendance and punctuality?'

Oh no! What did I say here? I took a chance.

'Very good, like you said. I'm local.'

He carried on writing, the cigarette ash falling onto the note pad.

'Why do you want to work here, Jacqueline?'

'Because it looks interesting. I'm keen to learn, I like make-up, I like helping people and I love babies. My mother was a nurse and she's shown me a lot of things as well.'

'Well, Jacqueline, the wage is two pounds and ten shillings a week. The hours are Monday to Friday nine to five thirty, with a late night until seven on Thursdays, and Saturdays nine until one.' He looked over his glasses, waiting for a reply.

I sat up straight.

'When can I start?'

His eyes squinted as the cigarette burnt away.

'Not so fast, there are others just as keen as you to interview – I will let you know by the weekend. What's your phone number?'

I lowered my eyes.

'I'm sorry, we don't have a phone.'

'Not to worry, I have your address.' He closed the notepad and removed the cigarette butt as I stood up to leave. Mrs Clayton and baby Paul had gone, but as we walked through to the front of the shop, three other people had taken their place.

'Oh, by the way,' I said, as we neared the door. 'Seventeen down, Holly.'

'What?' he said, opening the door and throwing the butt into a grate.

'The crossword – Christmas singer. It's Holly, not Carol.'

He stared at me. 'Holly?'

'Yes, Buddy Holly – he's a singer.' I stepped outside. The sun had vanished and it was pouring with icy rain.

* * * *

Mum was already home when I returned. I hung my wet coat on the back of the cellar door and fussed Shep, who had come to greet me.

'Do you think I'll get the job, Mum?' I asked, and threw myself into Dad's chair. 'He didn't ask for my leaving report.'

'Well that's a good thing, isn't it?' she replied, and continued putting the shopping away.

'But if he was really going to consider me, wouldn't he have asked for it?'

'What have you bought me for Christmas, Mum?' Josie asked, as she came into the room.

'You know I can't tell you that – you'll have to wait and see,' said Mum as she tut-tutted over the price of butter.

156

I glared at Josie.

'Do you mind? I'm talking to Mum, not you,' I snapped.

'But Ann Smith knows what she's getting,' she moaned.

I pulled a face at her. 'Shut up, mardy-bum, you can wait till Christmas, can't you?'

'You shut up. You can't tell me what to do.'

'Stop it! The pair of you –' Mum shouted.

'But Mum –'

'I shan't tell you again.' She banged a bag of sugar down on the table.

She looked across at me.

'There's a job advertised in the Star for an office junior at the coal board offices in town. Get yourself after that,' she glared, scooped the spilt sugar from off the table into her other hand and tipped it into the sugar bowl.

'But I don't want to work in an office, Mum. I want to work in that chemist's shop.' I slumped lower in the chair. 'And why haven't we got a telephone?' I snapped.

'A telephone? Don't talk ridiculous. What would we do with a telephone? Who would we call? Who would call us? We've only just got one put at the top of the road, thanks to me and Mrs Devonport.' She placed a jar of peanut butter in the cabinet. Josie licked her lips when she saw it.

'Can I have some, Mum?' She was kneeling on a chair at the table.

Mum took a slice of bread from the bread bin and spread it with peanut butter. She handed the slice to Josie, smiled and stroked her hair, then raised the cabinet flap to close it.

'Because – I'd get that job if we'd got a phone, that's why.'

Mum turned and laughed.

'Do you honestly think that having a phone will get you a job? Grow up, Jacqueline. Look around you – all these streets, all these people. None of them have a phone, yet everyone has a job.' She shook her head. 'I don't know how you think these days.'

I felt my face getting redder and redder.

'It's all right for you; you've already got a job. I haven't.'

'Jacqueline, you haven't tried. You've only been after one job. The paper is full of them, so get looking; I'm not keeping you unless you pay board.'

'Jesus, Mum, I haven't been left school a bloody week yet.'

'Don't you take the Lord's name in vain in this house, madam,' she shouted. 'And wash your dirty mouth out, coming in here with that language.'

Josie started grinning.

I pulled myself out of the chair, stormed past her and went upstairs.

'Who's a mardy-bum now?' she shouted.

* * * *

Later, I looked through the paper and chose two office junior positions. I wrote letters applying for both of them. Taking two threepenny stamps from the sideboard drawer, I stuck them on the envelopes and took them to the post box. Mum was taking Ian's temperature when I returned.

'What's the matter?' I asked, as I hung my coat up. I went over to Ian, who was quite pale and sitting in Dad's chair. He kept coughing.

'He says he's got a headache and his chest hurts. His nose is blocked too.' Mum took the thermometer from under his armpit and looked closely at it.

'Just under a hundred,' she said, then shook it and rinsed it under the tap.

I picked him up and cuddled him.

'What's the matter, love? Are you poorly?'

He placed his arms around my neck and began to cry. I rocked him in my arms.

The pressure cooker started to hiss so Mum went over and turned it down. I sat in the chair, nursing Ian.

'Do you want me to read you a story?' He didn't reply. His blue

158

eyes looked watery and heavy. I looked over at Mum. 'He's not well at all, is he?'

She set the timer for the pressure cooker.

'No he's not. It could be something he's picked up at nursery, but with this weather and the muck around here, it could be anything. I'll check his temperature again later. Your Dad wasn't well either when he went to work this morning. His chest's playing up again. Talking of chests, yours hasn't been too bad of late, has it?'

'Yes, it's been okay. Must be since I started smoking,' I grinned at her.

She didn't think it was funny. She put the cabbage on to boil and looked at the clock.

* * * *

Dad washed himself at the sink and went straight to bed with a hot water bottle when he came home. Mum had to go to work, so I took Dad some of the stew in a basin, but he didn't want it. I fetched the bucket and placed it beside the bed.

'Thanks, love,' he said, after the contents of his lungs had covered the bottom of the pail.

'You ought to eat something, Dad. Is there anything you fancy?'

'No love. Just let me sleep.' He lay back down, started coughing again and sat back up.

'What about some of that onion and mustard broth you have when you're poorly? Do you want me to make some of that?'

'I'll have some Beechams Powders, please, that's all.'

Downstairs, Josie sat writing her Christmas Cards.

'What's for supper?' she asked, as soon as I entered.

'Josie, you've only just had your tea. Don't ask how Dad is, will you?' I snapped, as I took some Beecham's Powders from the cupboard.'

She put down her pen.

'Is Daddy any better?' she asked.

159

'No he isn't, if you must know.' I mixed two packets of powder with a cup of warm water. 'Here, take this up to him while I see to Ian.'

I was mad at myself for snapping at her. She was such a bonny-looking girl. It was hard to believe she had a heart problem. She would be ten in a couple of weeks, almost as tall as I and much heavier-boned. I wondered if it was now time for our talk.

'Did he drink it?' I asked when she came back down.

'Yes, and then spewed it back up in the bucket. He's got some mucky hankies up there as well.'

'Why didn't you bring them down? They'll want soaking overnight in salt water.'

'I wasn't going to touch them.'

'They'll not hurt you,' I snapped.

Ian, asleep in Dad's chair, woke up coughing. His head was hot and he began to cry. His breathing sounded thick and heavy. I took his temperature; it had risen slightly. Then Dad shouted.

'Josie, watch Ian for me while I see what Dad wants.' I placed him back in the chair. Josie sat on the edge, stroking Ian's hair.

'What are you doing out of bed?' I asked, as I ushered Dad, who was wandering about in his long johns and woolly vest, back under the covers.

'Is there any clean hankies downstairs? There's none in my drawer.'

'There'll be some in the ironing pile – I'll go and have a look. You get back into bed.' I felt his forehead. It was hot.

I took some clean hankies upstairs and fetched the thermometer. I placed it under his tongue. He could hardly breathe.

I waited a couple of minutes and removed it. It read one hundred and two.

* * * *

160

'Josie, do you want to sleep in my bed tonight?' I took the tin of kaolin out from the pantry and put it to warm.

'Not likely, it's too cold up there in the winter.'

'Well it's too cold to take Ian up there, so you'll have to. Mum will have enough on with Dad tonight so I'll have to see to Ian.'

'I'll do it if Ann can stay.'

She watched as I removed the tin from the pan of boiling water and spread some of the contents over a piece of old clean nappy.

'Ann can't stay tonight – Ian and Dad are too poorly.'

'Well, can Shep sleep with me?'

'No.' I found a bandage in the cupboard and went back upstairs. 'Well, if you won't sleep in the attic, I'll have to take Ian up there, and if he gets any worse overnight and dies, you'll be to blame,' I shouted back down to her.

Josie gave in eventually, after moaning about having to sleep with all the pictures of ageing singers on the wall and dried onions hanging from the mirror.

I led her up into the attic and placed a hot water bottle in bed, and then found an extra blanket.

'Why haven't you got any of pictures of Cliff Richard?' she asked.

'Because I don't like Cliff Richard, that's why. Anyhow, you shouldn't be thinking about pop stars. You should be concentrating on your scholarship. It'll come round before you know it.'

She undressed. I couldn't believe my eyes. Her breasts were developing.

'What's the dried onions for, anyhow?' she asked, as she pulled on her nightie and climbed into bed.

'They're hung there for a reason – to stop the vampires getting you.'

She began to giggle.

'Mind you, all the power's gone out of them now, so there's no protection.'

The giggling stopped. Her eyes widened.

'Are there really any vampires, Jack?' She sat up in bed.

161

'Yes, and they're looking for mean little girls like you. Now get into bed and go to sleep.'

She threw my teddy bear at me.

* * * *

Dad and Ian had a bad night. By morning, they were both very poorly and running high temperatures. Mum gave me threepence to phone the doctor.

Josie survived the night in my attic but was refusing to talk to me, and then shouted her anger when I told her that we wouldn't be celebrating Christmas this year, with Ian and Dad being so ill.

'Stop tormenting her, Jacqueline,' said Mum, looking annoyed as she washed the pots. She turned to Josie. 'Of course we'll be having Christmas, love.'

I was drying the dishes and shaking my head at Josie behind Mum's back.

'Mum, she's shaking her head at me.'

Mum turned and caught me grinning. I jumped out of the way as she swung the dish-cloth at me.

'Stop it, the pair of you. I've got enough on my plate with your dad and Ian, without you two getting on my nerves.' She emptied the water from the bowl down the sink and banged it on the draining board.

'And you.' She looked at me. 'You ought to have more sense.' She snatched the tea towel from me and wiped her hands. Shep jumped up at the commotion.

* * * *

It was twelve o'clock when the doctor arrived. He took both their temperatures and listened to their chests, and then wrote a prescription for Dad for the usual brown medicine and the thick linctus, and something similar, of a lesser dose and strength for Ian.

162

He said to carry on with the nursing and poultices, and that he would call back tomorrow.

I took Josie with me to Hillsborough and handed in the prescriptions at the Co-op chemist. I wondered if I should have gone to the chemist where I'd been for the interview, but then I thought, perhaps not. While waiting, we looked in the other departments, and I bought Josie a Bunty comic, some new crayons and a bar of Fry's Five Boys Chocolate.

* * * *

The following morning, Dad and Ian were no better. The doctor was due but wouldn't arrive until later. Meanwhile, the Saturday morning cleaning ritual continued. Mum had washed the front door and was now rubbing the windowsill and step with donkey stone. I was cleaning the front room and tormenting Shep with a yellow duster.

A bright red sports car suddenly appeared in the street. Curtains twitched. It was rare for any car to come down the street, never mind a sports car. It pulled up in front of our door, and the driver got out. It was Mr Fox, the man from the chemists.

He was wearing a camel overcoat, a matching flat cap and leather driving gloves. Although his shoes were highly polished, I knew his trouser turn-ups would be full of cigarette ash.

'Good morning,' he said. 'Is this where Jacqueline lives?' Mum looked surprised. I knew she'd be thinking *what's she been up to now?*

I stayed indoors, hiding behind the net curtain. I was wearing a pinny and had no make- up on.

'Yes, she's in the front room. Do you want to see her?' Mum replied.

'No, that won't be necessary. Will you give her this envelope, please?'

He got into his car and drove away.

'I wonder who that was,' Mum said, as she came indoors, looking at the envelope.

'It's the man at the chemist where I went for that job.' I held out my hand for the letter. Ripping it open, I began to read.

'I've got it! Mum, I've got the job! I start on January the fifth.' I chucked the letter in the air, grabbed hold of her and gave her a big hug. 'I'll go up and tell Dad.'

Dad was pleased, and seemed to be a little better. The doctor, when he arrived and examined him, agreed and said he was managing to hold his own, and so was Ian. He told us to continue with the medication and that he would come again after Christmas, which was now only two days away.

* * * *

Christmas was a subdued occasion, as Dad and Ian's health took precedence. As the New Year came, both of them had a setback and their health deteriorated. The news from the doctor wasn't good. The medicines were no longer working, and pneumonia had set in. He said there were some new drugs now available but he'd not prescribed any yet. He added that he would look into it and talk it over with a colleague.

It was eight thirty on Monday morning when the doctor returned, before attending his surgery.

'Mrs Campbell, I have brought you two prescriptions for the new medicines I told you about. I have no samples. Otherwise, I would have brought those.' He went upstairs to see Dad and Ian.

I had applied my make-up with precision for my first day at work and was wearing a purple jumper with a tight black skirt and stiletto heels. Mum said they would be killing me before the day was over.

The doctor came back down and looked at Mum.

'They will need to start the medication as soon as possible.' He handed her the prescriptions. Mum and I looked at them, and the scribbled writing, which didn't make any sense. 'Must dash. I have to open the surgery, but I'll be back tomorrow. I'll let myself out.' He made his way to the door, with Shep nipping his heels as he left.

I left shortly afterwards to start my new job.

* * * *

I was waiting on the doorstep when Mr Fox arrived.

'Happy New Year,' I said, shivering, as he unlocked the door and went inside, switching on the lights. The shop filled with a fluorescent glow as we entered.

'Hmm! Oh, yes, Happy New Year,' he replied.

The assistant I had seen at the interview followed us. Within minutes, customers from the nearby surgeries began filling the shop.

'Doreen will see to you,' Mr Fox said as he disappeared into the dispensary. We hung our coats in a cupboard and Doreen handed me a pink overall similar to hers, except it was miles too big.

'I'll be back in a minute,' she said. 'I'll just collect the prescriptions,' and went into the shop to attend to the customers.

'I have two prescriptions here,' I said, when she came back.

She took them and placed them with the others in the dispensary.

'What have I to do first?' I asked.

She led me into the kitchen and pointed to where the cleaning utensils were kept.

'You can empty and clean the glass cabinet at the front of the shop and dust the items before replacing them. I'll have to leave you to it as I have to serve the customers and help in the dispensary.'

I emptied the shelves and cleaned the glass but instead of putting everything back in rows, I displayed them so they looked much more tempting.

Mr Fox suddenly came out from behind the counter.

'Jacqueline,' he called. 'Did you bring these prescriptions in?'

'Yes,' I replied. 'They're for my dad and my brother. They've got pneumonia.'

He looked at me over his glasses. 'They need to be on this medication straight away.'

'Yes, the doctor said so. I told Mum I'd bring the medicine at lunch time.'

He looked at his watch. 'I think you'd better take them now,' he said.

'But I've only just arrived, and I haven't finished my display.'

He looked at the work I had already done and smiled.

'You can finish it when you come back. Take these medicines home.'

I took off my overall and put my coat on.

'I'll be as quick as I can.'

I dashed out of the shop and ran all the way down the hill and through the park. Mum was right. My feet were already aching and it was only ten o'clock.

'What on earth's happened?' said Mum, a look of alarm on her face.

'I've brought the prescriptions. Mr Fox said they had to start them straight away.'

I made sure Mum gave them the correct doses, changed my shoes and dashed back to work.

'My, you have been quick,' said Mr Fox as I gave him some prescriptions that the customers in the shop handed me when they saw me going behind the counter.

He poured some liquid from one of the large bottles I had seen at my interview into a medicine bottle, and wrote out a label for it.

'I've never seen bottles as big as that,' I said, as he replaced the heavy bottle on the bottom shelf.

'Winchesters – they hold half a gallon,' he said, pushing his specs back up his nose. Doreen was busy counting tablets into a small bottle, and the shop doorbell kept ringing.

'It's always like this first thing in the mornings. It quietens down after eleven.' He stuck the label on the bottle.

'Have I to carry on with the cabinet, or is there anything else I can do?' I asked.

'Finish the cabinet and then make some tea.'

I did as he said, and it did quieten down a little after eleven. Doreen showed me more of the shop and talked me through my other duties. She told me my display was very good. I felt so proud.

There was another glass-fronted cabinet in the shop I hadn't previously noticed. It contained a large selection of stationery and books. Large, slim, brightly-coloured children's picture books. The illustrations were clear and vivid. I picked one out and thought it would be perfect for Ian.

I asked Mr Fox if I could buy one for my brother and asked if he would be so kind as to stop the half-crown payment out of my wages.

'What a lovely man,' said Mum when I took the book home at lunchtime and told her that Mr Fox had given it to me as a gift for Ian as he was so poorly.

'You've got a good job there, so look after it,' she said. 'Don't be taking time off – you've a responsibility now.'

'No, I'll not. I love it. I don't ever want to leave.'

* * * *

The new medicines worked on Dad and Ian. When they were well enough, they both had to go for chest X-rays where they found patches on their lungs.

The doctor told Dad that he had to stop working. Dad said it was out of the question with three children, and he was back at work within two weeks. It took a long time before he fully recovered.

As for Ian, his teeth rotted and fell out within a year. The doctor said it was due to the Tetracycline and Ian's general poor condition, and that his second teeth, when they came through, would be unaffected.

* * * *

Lynn and I met up and talked about our new jobs. Lynn was in an office and hated it. She had made new friends and began seeing more of them, as I couldn't get out as much, owing to Dad and Ian being ill for so long. I also spent a lot of time helping Josie with her homework.

Lynn and I began to go our separate ways. With our new jobs, different people came into our lives, and we drifted away from the regular crowd. Even Walt and I outgrew each other, and yet I missed the kisses and cuddles while standing in the darkness of our entry, lit only by the faint glow of the streetlight.

I loved the sensation of being in someone else's arms, other than those of my family: Walt's gentle kisses, with long silences in between. Was this what marital love was all about? To love and be loved all of the time?

Lynn and I still went to the pictures together occasionally, travelling farther afield and meeting different lads. Our mothers were forever warning us of pregnancy if we allowed boys to "go all the way."

Mum said that if any relationship with a boy became serious, I had to make sure they put a rubber sheath on their "thingy".

'Do you mean a prick?' I asked.

'Don't use that word, it's disgusting,' she replied.

Dad said I shouldn't bother with any lad who wanted to meet him inside the cinema.

'Always meet them outside and make sure they pay,' he stressed.

17

When spring came, prior to my sixteenth birthday later in the year, we decided to go on holiday. Lynn wouldn't go, as her new friend couldn't afford it and Christine's parents wouldn't let her go.

I cleared it with Mum and Dad, and Mum promised to look after Shep. Hazel and I looked through the advertisements in the Sheffield Star. There were so many to choose from, and we eventually chose a boarding house run by a Mrs Jennings in Blackpool.

I posted a one pound postal order as a deposit for the two of us for a week's holiday during the summer.

The balance of two pounds ten shillings each was payable on arrival. This was the first time we had been away without our parents.

Mrs Jennings took our payment balance as soon as we arrived, and showed us to our room. It had a double bed with a washbasin in the corner, a chair, a wardrobe and a dressing table with cigarette burns on its top.

'The bathroom is on the floor below. As it is shared, please refrain from putting on your make-up and doing your hair whilst in there, and use as little water as possible, otherwise there will be none for the other guests. Breakfast is at nine o'clock sharp, and dinner at five. The house is not to be occupied by guests between ten a.m. and four p.m. There is no late night key, so please make sure you return no later than eleven.'

'Yes, Mrs Jennings,' we chorused, as if we were back in school. As soon as she left the room, we burst into hysterics and threw ourselves on the bed. The view from the window overlooked the back of a hotel. We didn't care. We didn't intend to spend much time in the room.

It was the Scottish holiday weeks. Our intention was to chat up as many Scottish lads as we could.

On the first evening, we strutted down the Golden Mile dressed to impress. I was wearing a "shocking" pink full circle felt skirt, which had an image of a black poodle with blue glass eyes sewn onto the skirt. A collar and lead made from black ribbon hung around its neck, which ran all around the bottom of the skirt. I wore it with a black and white checked blouse and a black elasticated waspie belt.

Hazel wore a similar skirt in peacock blue, with a white blouse, and as we were going to be walking a lot, we wore our ballerina flatties.

There were cars parked along the side of the road and we looked for a posh one.

'Here, Hazel, this one.' We stood alongside it and looked into our handbags, waiting for a couple of good-looking lads to walk by. 'Here's two now,' I said, as two lads came over.

'You had the keys,' said Hazel.

'No, you had them,' I replied.

'Nice car you got there,' said one of them, in a broad Scots accent.

Hazel and I glanced at each other and grinned.

'Oh, hello, didn't see you coming. Yes, we seem to have misplaced our keys,' we said, as we fumbled in our handbags.

'See if yours'll fit, Craig,' said the other lad with a similar accent.

He took out a key and reached to the car door.

'That's a room key,' I said, opening his hand. We burst out laughing, and they introduced themselves.

'Where are you from, then?' I asked the tallest, Tony, as the four of us walked towards the Pleasure Beach.

'Paisley,' he replied. 'Whur are you two hens frae?'

Hens? We'd been called chicks before but never hens. I gave Hazel a wide-eyed glance.

'London. We're fashion models for Mary Quant.' I had no idea

170

who Mary Quant was, but had read somewhere that she was an up and coming designer who would soon take over the fashion market.

Hazel looked across at me and grinned. 'We're doing a photo-shoot on the pier tomorrow – you can come and watch if you want.'

'Och aye, an' I suppose you'll be giving us a lift home in the Bentley,' laughed Craig, and nodded back towards the car.

We had our photographs taken standing beside the Laughing Sailor in his glass case as we entered the Pleasure Beach.

'Where do we start?' I asked, as the crowd of like-minded people pushed past us.

'Come on,' said Craig. 'Let's start with the Funhouse.'

We paid at the kiosk and entered via the moving staircase, laughing, as we seemed to be taking more steps backwards than forwards. Walking the cake-walk and through the rolling barrels was almost impossible. We collapsed in a heap with a few more unfortunates, laughing hysterically at our joint predicament as we tumbled around in the bottom of the ever-turning barrel. The Hall of Mirrors came next. Our sides and jaws ached as more laughter came with the sight of the distorted images.

On leaving the Fun House, we ate hot dogs and then went on the Donkey Derby. None of us won anything. Craig won a coconut on the coconut shy and then dropped it while we were on the Grand National. I nearly threw up on someone while rushing to get off the new Wild Mouse ride. I'd left my stomach on the last turn.

We tested our non-driving skills on the Dodgem Cars, bumping each other. The smell of oil and rubber filled our noses as the cars trundled over the grease-slicked base, while the overhead electric mesh sparked as it powered the cars.

'Let's try the Ghost Train,' said Hazel, and placed herself at the back of the queue. We joined her and took money from our purses while the lads felt in their pockets.

The cars banged through the first set of doors into a darkened area, jolting and jerking around sharp bends, avoiding mirror images at the last second. Dangling gauze strips crept over our heads and faces, as the rickety carriage trundled along its track, banging and rocking through a maze of dark tunnels.

Screaming ghouls and ghosts appeared at every turn. We had to stop on for another ride, as we didn't see much the first time. The lads took advantage of the darkness, putting their arms around us and kissing us.

We finished off our evening on the Waltzer, with its wildly spinning tub-shaped cars rolling over the slopes and dips, as an over-enthusiastic attendant, legs wide apart, rode the moving floor, collecting fares, and then spinning the carriages and occupants into oblivion.

We had to hurry to get back before Mrs Jennings locked the door. The lads walked us back to our digs, where we found a dark corner and shared a few kisses, but when it got to hands down your blouse and up your skirt, we said goodnight.

* * * *

The following day, Hazel and I walked along the front. The smell of hot-dogs and fish and chips was making us hungry, and it wasn't even eleven o'clock. We had a plate of cockles and mussels from the sea-food stall, and then decided to look in Madame Tussaud's, where we found that the models were poorly made and didn't look a bit like the famous people they were supposed to represent, but the gruesome Chamber of Horrors really freaked us out.

The Freak Show posters for the Two-Headed Giant, Bearded Lady and Girl in a Goldfish Bowl aroused our curiosity, but our money was running out and we still had to see Adam Faith, and Emile Ford and the Checkmates. While we were deciding, a family of Dwarfs surrounded us. I found these little people scary. Hazel laughed. The little people held our hands and asked us if we had any questions.

'How does the woman get into the goldfish bowl?' I asked.

'You'll have to go inside to see,' said the small woman holding my hand. She let go and looked into her child-sized handbag, pulled out a packet of cigarettes and lit one.

We paid our sixpences and went inside. The exhibits were fascinating, probably originally from Madame Tussaud's, and mechanized in some way.

Curiosity again got the better of us and we had to see what the strip-tease girls did. The next show began in five minutes, so we queued; the only females in a line of men. We made our way to the front as if we were at a football match, and waited.

The curtains drew back. A girl not much older than us lounged on a chair. A large swathe of black and red damask fabric was draped over what was probably an old kitchen chair. Her legs were crossed and a strip of muslin hung loosely over her breasts and thighs. The curtains closed after a few minutes and then opened again to show another girl in a different pose.

Four more girls appeared before the curtains closed for the final time. The men licked their lips and one rubbed his crotch as they made their way to the exit. Hazel and I stood there, waiting.

A man came over to see why we hadn't left.

'Is that it? We haven't seen anything we haven't got ourselves,' I said to him.

He looked at us as if we were from the loony bin.

'Huh?' He scratched his head. 'What did you expect?'

I didn't know what to expect.

'More than that,' I replied. 'We could do that, just standing there. Why aren't they dancing or moving? You might as well just have a poster display.'

He rubbed his chin and looked us over.

'Ahh! I know what it is. You're looking for a job.' His eyes lit up.

Hazel and I laughed in his face.

'Not likely. We wouldn't do that for all the tea in China.'

'Look girls, come back in a couple of years when you've got a bit more up here.' He raised his hands up to his chest. 'Now come on, let's have you out of here, we've another show starting in five minutes.'

He ushered us to the exit.

We collapsed with laughter when we got outside, then went quiet as we realised we didn't have the breasts required for a strip-tease show.

* * * *

We spent time looking at the cheeky postcards displayed outside the shops. Every time we stopped, someone would be looking and laughing.

'Look Ethel, how about this one for our Alec and June?' or 'Have you seen this one Joan? It's just right for our Fred.'

We too bought cards and sent them to our parents. After all, Blackpool was a long way away from home.

The placards for all the different variety shows were colourful and inviting, but we didn't want to see Eddie Calvert and Alma Cogan. We were on our way to The Hippodrome.

On arriving, we joined the long queue, and finally entered. Our seats were at the back, where we could hardly see the stage. We screamed and chanted 'We want Adam,' throughout the warm-up acts.

When Adam Faith finally appeared, with the John Barry Seven as his backing group, we were hoarse, and couldn't scream any more, even when he sang our favourite hits, 'What do you Want', 'Someone else's Baby' and 'Poor Me'.

We sauntered back to our B&B after the show, tired and yet elated.

* * * *

The following evening, there was dancing on the pier. It was crowded. People had come from the surrounding areas to listen to the DJ play the top hits.

The music was loud and no one could hear themselves speak. As

174

soon as we finished one dance to have a rest, another record would come on which we couldn't resist.

The Everley Brothers sang 'Cathy's Clown', Eddie Cochran sang 'Three Steps to Heaven', 'Ain't Misbehavin'' by Tommy Bruce, and they played Jimmy Jones, and Johnny and the Hurricanes, along with Brenda Lee and Connie Francis.

We staggered back to Mrs Jennings', our feet covered in blisters, and sang 'Shakin' all over' as we made our weary way to the top floor and our bed.

* * * *

The week was almost over. Walking into town, our blistered feet crushed into shoes that fitted yesterday but didn't today, was agonizing. There were gifts and sticks of rock to buy.

We had promised ourselves a visit to the fortune teller Gypsy Rose Lee, and had decided to see her before shopping for gifts. We stopped and checked how much money we had left. When we arrived at her booth, there was a notice on the door stating: "CLOSED OWING TO UNFORSEEN CIRCUMSTANCES". We were disappointed but saw the funny side of it and went on to do our shopping in Woolworth's.

I bought Dad a stick of rock and a packet of humbugs. For Mum, a silver-painted model of Blackpool Tower. For Josie, a small brooch shaped like a book, which when opened, had ten small pictures of Cliff Richard, and for Ian, a Bat Masterson gun holster set.

This was our last night, and our money was almost spent. Walking down the Golden Mile, we bumped into the Scottish lads. We walked with them a while and called into the Brunswick. They bought us a lager and lime each, served in tall glasses that looked like vases.

'What if the coppers come in? We're underage.'

'Better get a glass of orange juice and place that in front of you,' said Tony.

They offered us cigarettes, which we placed in the new cigarette holders we had bought.

'What time's your train leave tomorrow?' Craig asked, and then took a long swig of McEwans.

'Twelve o'clock, what time do you leave?'

'Not till three in the afternoon – we'll most likely spend the time in here if we've any money left, eh Tony?'

'Aye, we might just manage a couple o' pints.'

They walked us back to Mrs Jennings', where we kissed, long and lovely. They didn't try anything else this time. We said goodnight and promised to write and meet them next year.

* * * *

'Is this the train to Sheffield Victoria?' I asked the guard.

'Yes, you've only just made it,' he said, lowering his flag and whistle.

We ran along, bumping into arriving holidaymakers. The air and the platform vibrated, as the massive black engine, spitting steam and smoke from various pipes and vents, waited to begin its long haul.

Finding the third-class coaches, we stepped aboard and pushed our way along the corridor.

'There are no seats left, love,' said a young woman, her face tanned. She was heavily pregnant and was sitting on her suitcase, three wide-eyed small children clinging to her skirt.

Our suitcases were too small to sit on, so we looked in the nearest compartment to see if there was any room in the overhead luggage racks, but they too were full.

We heard the sound of the guard's whistle, and the train lurched as it began its journey.

Everyone standing was jolted violently against the person standing next to them.

I looked down the corridor. It was impossible to move. Suitcases, prams and pushchairs holding numerous children blocked the aisle. Standing passengers were hanging on to whatever they could, knuckles white with the strain. One of the coach's window straps that held the glass in place was broken, and thick black smoke poured in. Some men tried to fix it with empty cigarette packets and matchboxes, to no avail.

It wasn't long before the train picked up speed, and the sounds of chuff-chuff-chuff changed to clickety-clack, clickety-clack as the cast iron wheels rolled over the expansion joints.

* * * *

'I want to go to the lav,' said one of the boys with the young woman.

'I told you to go before we got on,' his mother snapped as she looked up and down the crowded corridor.

'But Mum. I need to do a number two.' His face screwed up.

'For God's sake, Billy!' Her voice was agitated as she looked at the other two children in despair.

Seeing the urgent look on his face, I took hold of his hand.

'I'll take him for you.'

She looked relieved. 'Thanks, love. I'd be ever so grateful.'

Hazel stayed with the cases while I pushed my way along the corridor.

'How old are you, Billy?' I asked.

'Six, and I've got to go quick.' He hopped from one foot to the other.

I tried the door – locked.

'Hey, there's a queue. Get to t'back,' angry voices snapped.

'Been in there ages,' said someone sitting outside the toilet door. Billy began to whimper.

'Hey, you in there,' I banged on the door. 'Come on out – someone's desperate to use the toilet.' I banged on the door again.

The crowd of people lost their footing and jostled together as the train crossed tracks.

'If you don't come out, I'll fetch the guard,' I shouted through the door, knowing it would be impossible for him to get through the crowded corridor.

The door slowly opened and three people came out. Billy dashed in.

'Hey, we were waiting before you.'

* * * *

The train rocked on over the miles. Carriages lurched; people moved as one. Three hours after leaving the sea air of Blackpool and traveling through the clear Pennine air, we could now see the grey-yellow smog hanging in a thick pall over Sheffield.

We took turns to place our heads through the broken window, retreating quickly at the sudden deafness caused by the noise of the engine, and at the thick grey and black smoke rushing in when we entered the tunnels.

Eventually, the train slowed and pulled into Victoria Station. Our feet and legs ached as we walked down the long embankment to catch the bus. The trams had now come to the end of their days in our areas.

We waited for what seemed like an eternity. Hazel's bus arrived first. We arranged to meet the following Saturday. The bus to take me home followed later.

I hopped off the bus at the top of our street. Some kids were marking out hopscotch in the road with a piece of broken ornament they were using for chalk. Some girls had a washing line stretched across the street and were using it as a skipping rope.

'Once you get in, you can't get out, unless you tell your sweetheart,' they chanted, as the girls took turns to jump in and out at the right time. Some boys were playing Tin-Can Tommy, walking on cans they had tied to their feet with string. Others were playing Leapfrog or football, using the works gates as a goal. All had scabs and grazes on their knees, boys and girls alike.

Mothers appeared at the end of the entries, calling the kids in for tea. I was home.

Once indoors, I dropped my case, kicked off my shoes and kissed

Mum. I went into the front room to greet Dad, who was watching cricket on the telly.

The postcard I had sent stood on the mantelpiece. Shep made a fuss as if I had been gone forever, and Ian came over and gave me a hug. He only wanted to see if I'd brought him anything back.

'Where's Josie?' I asked, looking over at Mum.

'Across at Ann's – she'll be back soon. Have you had a good time, love?' She handed a plate of pork pie and buttered crusty bread to Dad, then looked at me. 'You're not very brown. Do you want some pork pie?'

'Yes please, I'll just unpack a few things first.'

'We had a bit of good news while you were away,' said Mum as she cut into the pie.

'What, Dad's won the football pools at long last?'

I pulled my gifts from the case.

A big smile spread across her face.

'Josie's passed her scholarship.'

18

I returned to work on the Monday. Mr Fox said that as I was excellent at the displays and that my handwriting was exceptionally neat, would I like to paint some posters for the shop window? He also said that we had sold a lot more cosmetics since my arrival, and that the younger generation loved how I showed them how to apply make-up correctly.

And I did. I loved making up their eyes like Elizabeth Taylor's or Sophia Loren's, and giving them a Brigitte Bardot pout. He added that I would be getting a pay rise on my sixteenth birthday.

I told Mum and Dad what Mr Fox had said, but they were more interested in Josie going to the City Grammar school. I was pleased for Josie and still wanted to help her as much as I could, but she said it wouldn't be necessary, as she now knew more than me, and from now on she was to be called Jo.

* * * *

Shep was now seven months old.

'He's bleeding,' I said to the vet. 'And he doesn't cock his leg up to wee, he squats.'

'Let me have a look at him. What's his name?'

'Shep,' I replied, and lifted him onto the table.

I could hear the dogs that had followed us barking outside.

The vet gave me a strange look. 'How long have you had him?'

'Since he was six weeks old,' I replied. 'Is it serious?'

'Yes, it is serious – your dog is a bitch.'

I looked at him and wanted to fade away.

'A girl, a female?'

I felt my face turning red.

He nodded, and placed Shep on the floor.

'Yes, and if those dogs outside get their way, she will be a pregnant one.'

He went on to tell me the facts of life regarding dogs and bitches and suggested spaying, but the cost was far too high. Mum would never pay it, and I couldn't afford it. The consultation had cost most of my wages.

'Well, when she comes into season, you must keep her indoors, and only take her out on a lead. It's only twice a year.'

I took her back home, keeping her close to my side, while the other dogs pestered us. Then Mum and Dad had a row about the noise the stray dogs were making, waiting outside our house all night.

I was afraid they wouldn't let me keep her. After a sleepless night, I vowed that if Shep had to go, so would I.

Mum and Dad bought me a Philips record player for my sixteenth birthday, along with ten records. I was so thrilled, never before had I received such a gift.

Except for work, I didn't leave the house for weeks. Lynn, Hazel and Christine came round and we went up into my room in the attic, playing records, dancing to Duane Eddy, the Everley Brothers, Ricky Valance and Tommy Bruce.

'Turn that racket down,' Dad shouted up to us. 'I can't hear myself think.'

Jo complained that she couldn't do her homework, so I turned it up louder for spite. I begrudged turning my pay-rise over to Mum to buy Josie's school uniform and a hockey set, which would never be used, owing to her heart complaint.

'Why buy a hockey set if she's not allowed to play?' I argued.

Mum waved the paper in front of my face. 'Because it's on the list.'

'Not if you explain that she can't play such strenuous games.' I was furious.

'I'll not let her be shown up in front of the others. She's going to the City Grammar with everything on that list, so there. Let that be the end of it,' she snapped back.

'I wouldn't have got a set when I went to Chaucer though, would I?'

'Don't talk daft.' Mum's blue eyes darkened. 'You didn't do sports. You couldn't stand them...*Mum, write me a note to excuse me from netball, tennis, field games or whatever I don't want to do,*' she mimicked.

'That's beside the point, isn't it? What did I ever get when I was her age, eh?'

'Don't give me that. You never went short of anything.'

'No one helped me to get to grammar school, did they? Who played at school with Josie, eh? Who did it for me? No one helped me with my homework.'

'Things were different back then.'

'Oh yes, things were different all right. Jack do this, Jack do that, Jack see to Ian, Jack see to...'

I glanced around my bedroom.

'You can take the rotten record player back if that's all you bought it for, to soften me up.'

'You ungrateful bitch.' She slapped me across the face.

My other cheek burned just as hot. Rage poured through me. I swung open the wardrobe door and pulled out my clothes.

'Well, you'll not get another penny of board off me; I'm going to live with Auntie Doris.' I pulled the suitcase from the top of the wardrobe and began putting my clothes in it.

'Clear off to Doris's, but don't come back crying to me when it doesn't work out. Doris'll not keep you on two pounds a week. She spends that on cigarettes.'

'I'll be in good company then, won't I?' I shouted back and pulled my underwear out of the drawer and stuffed it in the case.

'If you're leaving home, you can take this lot with you.' She pointed at my bedroom walls and stormed off downstairs. 'And Shep,' she added.

I looked around the room at my pictures. Elvis and Adam, Buddy

Holly, Gene Vincent, Eddie Cochran. They were all laughing at me. I threw myself onto the bed and sobbed.

* * * *

It was ages before we spoke. An uneasy silence existed between us. We met briefly, as I came in from work and Mum left. I was unhappy. Yet neither of us would give in and apologise. It was only when Ian got Mumps and required a prescription that we began speaking again. Within the same year of him getting chicken pox, so did Josie, and so did I.

At sixteen, it was an awful thing to have. The doctor said that I was lucky to get away with only one pockmark on my face. Apparently, getting chicken pox when you are older is more serious, and can lead to facial disfigurement. Nevertheless, no amount of make -up covered the bullet hole in my forehead. I cursed Uncle Wilf for telling me that if I worked in the poultry shed, I would never get chicken pox. I was determined to never go out again. Apart from work, as that was the last place I would meet a potential boyfriend.

Later, when I'd fully recovered, I cut and shaped my fringe so it covered the hole in my head.

* * * *

Hazel and I went to a new club that had recently opened, Club 60. It was in the cellars of an old pub on Shalesmoor. The rough stone walls and ceiling were painted white. The largest room held the small stage. There was no dance floor as such, and dancing on the cobbled floor risked a broken ankle.

The other cellars were quieter, and were ideal for having a drink, a smoke and a chat.

Jimmy Crawford, a local lad and his band, played there regularly. He was so groovy, with his bleached blonde hair with a massive quiff and thick sideburns.

Hazel and I loved the club and started going every Saturday. We had dates galore. The downside was that the club didn't close until after the last bus had gone, so it meant walking home, as none of the lads we met had cars.

* * * *

One night, Hazel got talking to a lad who lived near her, who offered to walk her home. We were about to leave, when a lad who had asked me to dance earlier and I'd turned down, asked if he could walk me home. Why not? I thought.

Hazel and I said our goodbyes and the four of us left the building. Most of the people had already gone. We lit cigarettes in the doorway before we split. Greg placed his arm around me as we walked along Shalesmoor. I felt mean that I had turned him down earlier, just because he wasn't as handsome as Elvis or Adam Faith.

'Where do you live, Jackie?' he asked, as he took a deep drag on his cigarette.

'Near the Wednesday ground,' I replied.

He suddenly stopped, and turned to face me.

'Fuckin' 'ell,' he said, and looked at me as if I'd said Timbuktu.

'We'll have to do it 'ere then,' he said, and grabbed hold of my wrist, pulling me along the pavement and behind some old works railings.

I struggled to get away and burnt my wrist and new blouse as my cigarette fell from my hand.

'Stop it,' I cried, trying to pull away from him.

'Come 'ere.' He held on to my wrist and pulled me further into the yard. I began to scream, but he pulled me towards him and placed his hand over my mouth.

'You know you want it. Playing hard to get, eh?'

I had never experienced anything like this before. My heart beat heavily in my chest as I became aware and afraid of his strength. I pushed his hand away.

'You're mistaken. I'm not like that. Now let me go – please.' I looked around. It was dark and there was no one in sight. 'Let me go!' I screamed again, but his lips covered mine and he pushed his tongue into my mouth. The more I struggled, the tighter he held me. He pushed his hand under my blouse. I felt the buttons rip, and then his hand reached under my bra.

'You want warming up, is that it?' He bit my lip as he pulled his mouth away. 'Is this what you want? Huh?' His rough hand squeezed my breast. 'Come on, let's feel these tits.'

I began to cry. The railings were sticking into my back, and something was sticking into my front.

'Flat as a fuckin' pancake,' he mumbled, as he removed his hand and pushed it up my skirt and inside my knicker leg. He gasped as he felt my suspenders and came onto me even more.

I was sobbing and choking, but he wouldn't stop. I felt his hand move away. He placed it between us and began fumbling, and then I heard the sound of a zip unfastening. He grabbed my hand and placed it on his prick.

'That's what you're going to get.' He slobbered into my ear and held my hand firmly over it.

It was huge, wet and slimy. I could smell it. It stunk of piss and something else. I bit into his lip, but he still held on. I remembered what Dad had said about it being the most vulnerable part of any man, and if I was ever attacked, that was where to kick. I couldn't kick out, I was too near.

I stopped struggling.

'Okay,' I said. 'Let me get my breath.'

'That's better. Cooperate.' He released his grip on me as my hand slowly moved back and forth over his prick.

'Oh yes, that's it. See, you do want it, don't you?' His body relaxed.

Back and forth, I held on to his swelling prick, then gave it a quick wrench, as hard as I could, and pushed him off. He doubled over. I ran.

* * * *

I couldn't find the gap in the railings. It had to be near here. I fumbled along – it was too dark to see.

'You fuckin' bastard,' I heard him shout. 'I'll have you for that. I'll shove more than me fuckin' prick into you.'

'Oh God,' I swore. 'Where's the gap?' I could hear my heart thumping. This was worse than the fire. I could hear him coming after me. I daren't look back. He was gaining on me. I was wearing my stiletto heels, which didn't help, yet I dared not remove them for fear of the broken glass, rusty wire and scrap metal lying around.

I suddenly found the opening and dashed through. I had to get to the main road.

He was almost on top of me when I saw a car pulling away from the back of the Club 60. I ran into the road, waving my arms. It was a pink Zodiac. It pulled alongside me and stopped. I couldn't get my breath. I was crying with fear and relief and couldn't speak.

The blond-haired driver wound down the window.

'Are you alright, love?'

It was Jimmy Crawford. I still couldn't answer. I stood panting, sobbing, crying and shaking. My blouse was torn, my hair a mess, so was my make-up. A heel had come off my shoe and my stockings were torn. He looked behind me and saw the lad, who suddenly turned and walked the other way.

Jimmy looked at the woman sitting beside him and then back at me. 'Hop in, love. Let's get you home.'

* * * *

I never returned to the Club 60 for fear of meeting Greg. Hazel and I went to the Locarno in Sheffield instead, and the local cinemas.

I eventually dated different lads: a bricklayer, a motor mechanic, and a trainee mortician. That wasn't a success. I couldn't bear the thought of him touching me after he'd been handling dead bodies all day. I even dated the local milkman, something Mum arranged. I only went the once – he was so square, and a lot older than I was. I didn't want to be seen with someone over twenty. I didn't like how he kissed either. It was always wet and sloppy.

Whoever I was dating, I always took them home to meet Mum and Dad. There was only one time Dad went mad when I took someone home, and that was when I took home an Irish lad called Charlie, who worked on the travelling fair, which had come to Owlerton.

'An Irish navvy,' Dad said, after he'd left. 'I thought you'd more about you Jack, than to pick up someone like that.' He gave me a disgusted look.

'But Dad, I thought you'd like him, you both having the same name.'

He looked at me as if I'd told him that one day a man would land on the moon.

'And he's not laid a finger on me, not like Greg and that mortician fellow – he couldn't keep his hands to himself.'

'Don't go upsetting yourself, Charlie,' interrupted Mum. 'He'll soon be moving on.'

'And what if I move on with him?' I lowered myself onto a chair and lit a cigarette.

Dad started to rise.

'Sit down, Charlie, she's having you on.' She looked at me. The warning in her eyes was clear.

'I'm only going out with him to get free rides on the waltzer,' I said, and went to bed.

* * * *

The attacks of bronchitis, which had plagued me as a child, returned as I approached my seventeenth birthday. It didn't help that I walked back and forth to work, at least a mile each way, in all kinds of weather. Rain, sleet, gales, snow and ice, plus lunchtimes, as Mr Fox closed the shop for an hour. It was no wonder my hands and ankles were always chapped. I also smoked between twenty and thirty

187

cigarettes a day, sometimes Capstan Full Strength. Len, who married my cousin Brenda, got me onto them.

Mum kept telling me how stupid I was, and that I would end up like Uncle George, dead before fifty. I replied that I might take after Granddad and live until my seventies.

Hazel and I were at the Locarno one Saturday night, when I met Pete. He and his pal came over and split Hazel and me up. We were bopping to Bernard Taylor's band.

The dance floor was crowded, and it bounced with the beat. The girls wore full circle skirts with layers of stiffened petticoats underneath, neatly ironed blouses or black batwing tops, tucked into narrow waists with black waspie belts, most of them wearing stiletto-heeled shoes. The girls who couldn't dance in heels danced in their nylon stockings.

Pete was about five feet ten inches tall, with curly fair hair and blue eyes. He was wearing a royal blue fingertip jacket with velvet lapels, and tight black trousers. Not exactly Billy Fury, but near enough. We danced until we were exhausted, and then we went to the bar for a drink, sitting the next few dances out.

He held my hand while we talked about our work and families. He said he was a pipe fitter at Tinsley Wire, and was a year older than me. He too had younger brothers and sisters, and wasn't ashamed to admit that, as old as he was, he had to take his turn in looking after his siblings, as his father was dead and his mother cleaned offices in the evenings.

We had so much in common. I felt as if I had known him all my life.

The evening wore on and the band began to play the slower numbers. Leading me to the crowded dance floor, he held me in his arms as we moved to the sounds of, *Are you Lonesome Tonight?*, *Stranger on the Shore* and *It's Now or Never*.

We didn't know how to waltz. Most kids our age didn't, so we walked the "Creep", not moving more than two yards, my head resting on his chest. He smelled clean and fresh and held me close, his hand pressed gently but firmly across my back. I'd had smoochy dances before, but with Pete, the nearness of his body made me feel so different.

When he looked down at me and smiled, I wanted to stay in his arms forever.

We caught the last bus home and stood in our entry. He held me close, and when we kissed, it was with a passion I thought only happened in films.

I found myself responding. I held him tight and stroked the back of his hair, pulling him closer. I wanted more.

He suddenly pulled away.

'Oh God,' he muttered. 'I'd better control myself. Look what you've done to me.'

I couldn't see a thing – it was too dark, but I could feel his hardness and his body shaking.

'Jackie, you're so lovely,' he whispered in my ear, as he took hold of me again. I'd never heard my name pronounced that way before. His voice was soft, barely a whisper.

'I'd better stop, before I do something I'll regret.' He placed his hand on my shoulders.

His body shuddered. I didn't want him to stop. We kissed again.

In the dark entry at the bottom of our street, something in my body awakened, and I never wanted it to end.

* * * *

We arranged to meet the following Wednesday, outside the Park Cinema. I couldn't wait. I spent the next few days in a trance, always thinking about him. Sometimes I woke up in the middle of the night because I couldn't remember what he looked like. Even Mr Fox noticed and told me to concentrate. My attention span was short-lived. I'd drawn Mum's attention too.

'You mind what you're doing, and be careful. Remember what I told you about using something if it gets serious?' she warned.

189

* * * *

It wasn't long before I brought him home. Mum and Dad took to him straightaway, and so did Jo and Ian. Even Shep gave him a tail wag and her paw.

We were never alone in the house though. Mum didn't come in from work until after ten o'clock. She would watch television and read the newspaper until it turned midnight. Dad lit his last pipe of tobacco of the day at eleven and that too lasted until midnight.

Our romance ripened in the confines of our entry.

Weeks went by and Pete told he loved me. Things were getting serious. He was also becoming quite possessive and jealous, always asking me if I had been out with anyone else on the nights we didn't see each other. When I was out with him, he got upset if I spoke to the local lads that I knew. He kept trying to persuade me to have sex, but I wouldn't, as he refused to wear something. I would not betray Mum and Dad's trust. Our passion was becoming stronger, and sexual urges were more difficult to resist every time we met.

'Let's get married,' he said one night, when we were walking home from the cinema.

I stopped dead. 'Married?'

'Why not?'

I took hold of his arm, still in shock. 'When?'

'Next year. We'll get engaged at Christmas.'

We kissed in the middle of the street, clinging onto each other. I couldn't wait to tell Mum and Dad.

'You're a bit young, love,' said Mum. 'But he's a grand lad, and I hope you'll both be very happy.'

'An' you've my blessing as well,' said Dad, as he gave me a big hug.

I was so very, very happy. I was going to be married.

Four weeks later, four words from Mum ended it all.

19

I had been going to church for the past few weeks, somewhere I hadn't been since taking Josie to Sunday School, apart from Granddad's funeral and Brenda and Len's wedding.

Somehow I found solace and some comfort, even though I wasn't religious, having argued many times with Mum in the past.

'If there's a God, why does he allow such terrible things to happen in the world?' I would say.

Mum would reply with: 'The Lord moves in mysterious ways.'

'Yes, it's a mystery alright, as to why a peace loving God allows nations to massacre each other.'

* * * *

'I'm going to be a nun,' I said to Mr Fox, who was counting tablets into a small bottle, a Kensitas dangling from his lip.

'Ninety-nine, one hundred.' He screwed the top on the bottle, turned towards me and stared, his round friendly face showing concern.

'What's brought this on – the breakup?' He looked away and wrote the dosage instructions on a label.

'Why not? I'm seventeen, and I don't think I'm cut out for this sort of life.' I corrected myself. 'I don't mean working here – I love my job, and you've been so good to me and my family. It's the social side I don't think I'm cut out for, you know, marriage and babies and all that stuff.'

'Nothing to do with the break-up, then?' he asked, his eyes peering over his glasses. He licked the label and stuck it on the bottle.

'Fellas only want one thing.'

'Hmmm! Is that so? Have you visited the convent?'

The convent was just down the road from the shop. The sisters looked after homeless children. They often called in at the shop with prescriptions, or appealed to Mr Fox's good nature by asking for free items.

He rubbed his chin and picked up a Winchester of liquid paraffin.

'Mum says I've to put everything behind me and get back on with my life.' My lip quivered as the past came flooding back.

'Well, you're not going to thank me for this, but your mother is quite right.' he said, as he filled a medicine bottle with the thick clear liquid and wrote a label. The cigarette in his mouth had burned away, so he lit another one. He checked the labels on the bottles against the prescriptions and handed them to me. He was quiet, concentrating.

'Mrs Dean,' I called, as I took the bottles into the shop and placed the items in a pharmacy bag. 'That will be four shillings, please,' I said, as she came over to the counter.

'Four shillings, it's disgusting,' she complained. 'Having to pay double the price.'

'You have two items, Mrs Dean. That's why it's four shillings.'

She looked in her purse, which she clutched close to her chest, and counted out a two-shilling piece and two separate shillings. The shop was full, and the customers looked on as she handed over the money.

'Thank you,' I said, and passed her the medicines. She turned, mumbling, and left the shop.

I went back into the dispensary to see if any more prescriptions were ready.

* * * *

'Before you make a final decision, why don't you work with me in dispensary?' Mr Fox said, as I returned.

'What?' I was shocked. 'In the dispensary? But I don't know anything about medicines and reading prescriptions. They're in Latin, aren't they?'

'Nothing you can't learn if you put your mind to it.'

'But I haven't been to college or university so I'll not be able to.'

'I'll be the judge of that. Why don't you give it a try? I'll show you.'

'But I like being in the shop, serving the customers and doing the window displays…'

'You will still be able to work in the shop, and you can help me when the dispensary gets busy. Doreen is thinking of starting a family, so she could be leaving soon.'

The shop doorbell rang again.

'Think it over before contacting the Little Sisters,' he said, as he lit another cigarette, and I went to serve the customer.

* * * *

'She might get to be a doctor yet,' Dad commented sarcastically when I told them of Mr Fox's suggestion.

'He must think a lot of you,' Mum replied, a proud look on her face. 'I'm pleased for you, love.' She put her arms around me and gave me a hug. 'It'll do you good; help take your mind off other things. Why don't you come on holiday with us for a week? I've booked a caravan at Mablethorpe. The change will do you good.' She stroked my arms and tummy. 'Look at you, wasting away.'

'Thanks, Mum. I'll think about it.'

Things had moved on since I'd started courting. Most of my friends were courting themselves, or had already made holiday plans.

I decided to go with Mum and Dad, and I was glad I did, as I enjoyed it more than I'd thought, even though there were few people my age. The campsite provided plenty of entertainment, and I walked into town every day with Jo, Ian and Shep.

We ate fish and chips, hot dogs and burgers. But before the week was over, I had come down with bronchitis again. The train journey home was horrendous. The crowded train was thick with smoke and my chest was racked with pain. We all had to stand, and then some people moved to make room for Mum and Dad.

Jo was tired and kept swapping places with Mum. Ian cried all the time with toothache, and Shep hated it. She was barking and panting, trying to get comfortable in the overcrowded train.

* * * *

'You've got to stop smoking,' the doctor said as he wrote out a prescription for more Tetracycline tablets.

'But I have, doctor,' I replied, as my chest groaned and I felt as if my lungs had collapsed. A raucous cough came from somewhere deep inside me. I heaved, as the thick phlegm stuck in the back of my throat. I finally coughed it up, and spat it into the bucket beside my bed. It smelled of Dettol but contained thick brown gunge.

'You'll start again, though, as soon as you're well,' he said as he replaced his stethoscope and prescription pad back in his bag.

'Not this time, doctor. Enough's enough. Anyhow, you smoke and so does Dr. Moore.'

'Our lungs are in far better condition than yours.'

* * * *

Within two weeks, I was back at work and smoking again. I'd weighed seven stones on leaving school – I now weighed six and a half, the same as Jo, and I was becoming more depressed. Every evening, I stayed in my bedroom playing the same records over and over again. Roy Orbison, singing *Only the Lonely*. Elvis, singing *Blue Moon* and *Heartbreak Hotel*.

I knew I had to let go of the past. Mum, who had been the bearer of bad news, came to my room many times to find me in tears.

'Time heals, love,' she said every time, followed by: 'this time next year you'll have forgotten all about him.'

* * * *

I decided to help in the dispensary and started taking Wate-On, a multi-vitamin supplement, which Mr Fox had suggested. He also made a tonic mixture for me. He didn't tell me to stop smoking, being a smoker himself.

With new determination, I concentrated on learning everything about the dispensary and hoped it would take my mind off Pete. My heart was like an open wound. I never knew this type of pain could exist.

On Sundays, I walked miles over Wadsley Common with Shep. As we walked, I recalled the different scribbled words on the prescriptions. I recited the medical and Latin names repeatedly in my head: *1 nocte…One at night. T.D.S., ter die sumendum…Three times a day. Q.D.S., quarter die sumendus…four times a day – don't get it mixed up with quaque die which means every day.*

I soon learned the names of the medicines on the shelves and those locked in the D.D.A. cupboard. As I became more knowledgeable, Mr Fox allowed me to write out the dosage labels.

'Never take a filled prescription to the patient without allowing me to check it first,' he stressed. 'Place the items with the prescriptions on the corner of the bench.'

He watched me carefully as I read the prescriptions and chose the correct medications and counted out tablets, capsules and pills, placing them in the correct dispensing bottles.

For oral medicines such as linctuses and liquid paraffin, we used clear glass bottles.

Dark brown oval or hexagonal ribbed bottles were for lotions that were applied to the body, and not to be taken by mouth. That's why they were a different shape and were ribbed – even blind people could not mistake them for oral medicines.

'Good work, Jackie. You'll be mixing ointments and liniments before long,' said Mr Fox.

I loved my job and the new undertakings, and with my new responsibilities, Pete faded into the background.

* * * *

Lynn came round one evening. She told me it was one of her workmates' birthdays on Friday and that they were all going to a great pub they had found recently.

'There's a group on. Do you want to come with us?' she asked.

'Thanks, but I…'

'Come on, Jackie, it'll do you good.' She put her arm around me.

'Where is it?' I asked, 'It's not up Stannington, is it?'

'Jackie.' She frowned and removed her arm. 'Does it matter where it is? It's over. Now come on, it's a good laugh. We sit near the front and flick peanuts at the drummer.' Her eyes gleamed with devilment. 'And no, it's not near Stannington. It's on the Shirecliffe estate.'

I looked towards her. 'Did you say Shirecliffe?

'Yes, why?'

'Mum said I was conceived up there.'

* * * *

It was pouring with rain outside when I came home from work at lunchtime the following day. Mum was sitting at the table with a letter in her hand. She looked worried. I wiped my hair on a towel by the sink and changed my wet shoes.

'What's the matter, Mum?' I put my hands on her shoulders.

'I've got to have a hysterectomy.'

I slid onto a chair beside her.

'Since when?' I took hold of her hand.

'I didn't want to worry you, love. You've had enough on your plate recently.' Her blue eyes misted over as I squeezed her hand. She

196

felt in her pinny pocket for a hanky.

'But Mum, you should have told me.' I went over to the sink to fill the kettle, and looked at the back of her head, as I had done many times before. A few years ago, it had been completely auburn. Now it was turning grey.

A lump came into my throat. I couldn't bear the thought of Mum getting old. I must bring a hair colour for her, I thought, as I made the tea.

'Don't worry about me, love,' she said, as I placed a cup in front of her. 'What will be, will be.'

The inevitable question, the big C, was on my lips, but I couldn't pluck up the courage to ask. Then I felt angry. I sat back down beside her, annoyed that she hadn't told me about it earlier.

'Get yourself a sandwich, love, there's some potted meat and Spam in the fridge.'

'Do you want one making?' I asked as I opened the fridge door.

'No thanks. I'm okay with a cuppa.'

'I wish you'd told me earlier, Mum,' I took a bite of my sandwich and lit a cigarette.

'What could you have done if I had?'

I sighed, took a deep drag on my cigarette, and blew smoke towards the ceiling.

'How serious is it?' The cigarette had given me courage.

'They don't know yet, but they're not taking any chances. They're doing a full hysterectomy.'

'When?' I was being too abrupt with her. She didn't deserve it. I was still upset that she could keep something like this from me.

'Next week, at Jessops.'

'Next week? That's a bit quick. Does Dad know?' I finished my sandwich and cigarette.

'Yes, but he doesn't know the date. The letter only arrived this morning.'

* * * *

Mr Fox said it would be all right for me to adjust my hours accordingly. Ian could take himself to school, and Jo was quite capable of getting herself to the City Grammar.

I told Jo about Mum's forthcoming operation. She already knew what the operation entailed. We told Ian that Mum was going into hospital to make her tummy better.

'Is she going to have a baby?' he asked, acknowledging the news.

'I'd better not be!' Mum laughed. 'I honestly don't know where he gets it from.'

'Well if you're not having one, will you see if there are any spare, because I'd like a brother instead of two sisters.'

20

On Friday evening, Mum had gone to work, and Dad, after having his tea, was asleep in his chair. Jo was upstairs doing her homework and Ian was playing under the kitchen table in a den he had made.

I washed at the kitchen sink. I dressed in a pair of tight blue jeans, with a white blouse and Dad's Airforce-blue jumper, which was miles too big for me but made a great Sloppy Joe. A pair of black flatties completed the look. I put on my make-up, and as my hair had grown since my bubble and D.A. hairstyles, I swept it up in a beehive and secured it with hairgrips, pins, and hair lacquer supplied in a soft plastic bottle, which you had to squeeze to spray, and with a bit of luck, some would go on your hair.

I told Josie to take Ian to bed at eight o'clock and read him a story.

'What about my homework?' she replied with a shrug.

'It doesn't take all night, and it won't hurt for once,' I snapped. It still cost me two shillings, to make it worth her while.

Lynn arrived and I applied her make-up.

'It's a long time since you did this, Jackie, thanks. It always looks better when you do it.' She rose from the chair. 'Come on, we're meeting the others at eight.'

I grabbed my purse, cigarettes and matches and left the house.

* * * *

The concert room of the Five Arches pub was almost full when we arrived. Two of the other girls Lynn knew had already secured a table near the front, where the band was warming up. I was welcomed by them, and it felt good to be out again.

Lynn and I went to the bar and joined the queue. Two young men and a barmaid were behind the bar, struggling to serve the growing crowd.

'Two halves of bitter and a packet of peanuts, please,' I said when it was our turn, and pulled my purse from my jeans pocket.

'Are you eighteen?' the fair-haired barman asked, as his arm worked the pump.

I looked around.

'Are you talking to me?' I turned and faced him, handed him the money and passed one of the glasses to Lynn. 'Yes,' I lied. 'Are you?' I picked up my glass and walked away, laughing.

The room continued to fill up until there was standing room only. We flicked peanuts at the drummer's cymbal in between songs: *ping, ping, ping*. He grinned and shook his drumsticks at us. When it was their break time, he picked some of the nuts off the floor and stuffed them in his jacket pocket.

The crowd of people hushed somewhat as a couple of police officers entered the room. Alcoholic drinks placed on the tables were slid towards elders. Young eyes watched cautiously, us included, as the officers walked slowly around, scrutinizing faces and the drinks on the tables. Lynn and I stood up to go to the toilet. We lit cigarettes as we rose and made our way towards the back. We waited a while and then heard voices in the foyer.

'Honest, copper. I am eighteen, I was born in nineteen forty three,' a young male voice pleaded.

'Learned it off by heart, have you, son?' one of the officers replied.

We heard the outer doors open and close, and went back into the concert room, where the group had finished their break and were positioned back on stage. They played a few chords of the *Dixon of Dock Green* theme tune and the audience laughed. We took our seats back at the table. It didn't take long for the jovial atmosphere to resume.

An old woman of around forty came round selling raffle tickets for a first prize of a matching chrome-plated Swan Brand teapot, milk jug and sugar basin, and a second and third prize of a bottle of whisky and half a bottle of gin. Sparks from the cigarette dangling from her lips caused her to squint as she spoke, bright red lipstick like a gash across her face as it ran into the deep creases around her lips.

We bought a shilling's worth of tickets. The woman gave a chesty cough as she bent over and tore the tickets from the booklet, her dyed blue-black hair showing grey roots.

* * * *

'He's been chatting me up,' said Lynn, as she returned from the bar with more drinks.

'Who has?' we asked, intrigued.

'The barman, the one with the dark hair.' She glanced over to the bar area. We could just see him through the smoke-filled air. He was serving someone, but he looked over and waved at Lynn. We all waved back. Lynn's face turned bright red.

'You rotten pigs,' she said, as she sat down.

The singer and lead guitar played a few tunes before stepping back to allow the drummer a drum solo. We whistled and clapped as he finished on a roll. Then he reached in his pocket and pelted us with peanuts.

* * * *

'We've got a couple of birthday celebrations in here tonight,' said the singer, calling for attention as he tapped on the microphone. 'We've got Harold at fifty. Stand up Harold and let's have a look at you.'

Harold reluctantly stood up. The crowd applauded.

'Well, Harold, you don't look a day over forty nine,' the singer laughed, followed by the audience. 'Who else have we got?' He glanced down at the scrap of paper in his hand and then around the audience. 'Christine – who is eighteen today. Where are you, Christine? Stand up.'

The drummer kept the tempo up by tapping his foot gently on the bass drum pedal and flicking the brush over the snare drum.

Christine blushed as the singer teased.

'She's here,' we shouted, trying to get her to stand up.

The singer's eyes found her. 'So, you're old enough to drink legally now, Christine?'

The drummer gave a "boom-boom" on the bass drum.

'Stand up, Christine, let the landlord see who's been coming in here for almost a year and drinking pints.' Laughter reverberated around the room. Christine blushed even more and stayed put in her seat.

'Nah, she's not going to stand up folks, but give Christine and Harold a big round of applause for being good sports,' said the singer as he looked at the audience and started clapping.

'Just a minute, before we get back on with the show, what's your favourite song, Christine?' He looked towards her. 'I'm not going to ask you to stand up, just tell me your favourite song.'

'Go on Christine,' we urged.

'Jealousy by Billy Fury,' she called.

'What was that?' He placed his hand behind his ear.

'Jealousy, by Billy Fury,' we all chorused.

The singer stepped back, looked at the rest of the group and nodded. The audience quietened, then erupted into laughter as the band began to play and the singer sang...

'My old man's a dustman – he wears a dustman's hat...'

* * * *

The evening eventually ended, and at ten minutes to ten, the landlord called for last orders. Loud groans rumbled throughout the room and a mad scramble took place at the bar. The band played their final number, and as the drummer played the closing beats, we pelted him with peanuts again.

Ten minutes later, the landlord rang the large ship's bell.

'Time, ladies and gentlemen please.'

People finished their drinks, and the concert room emptied, cold air creeping in with the opening door. The drummer and singer came over and began talking to us.

'Can we have your glasses, please? It's ten past ten.' The landlord's voice boomed over the speaker system. The few remaining customers removed their spectacles and raised them in the air.

The other girls in our group left to catch their buses. Lynn and I finished our drinks and made our way to the toilet. The two barmen were talking together and watching us as they collected the bottles and glasses and emptied the ashtrays.

Lynn and I shivered as we left the toilet and made our way to the outer doors. The smoke swirled out as the cold November smog and smell of fish and chips rushed in. A few people stood in the doorway, fastening their coats, tying scarves and saying farewells.

'I enjoyed tonight, Lynn, even though we didn't win the raffle.' I laughed.

'Just as well, what would we have done with those prizes?'

'Given them to our mothers, I suppose.'

We moved towards the door, following the crowd. Someone came behind us and placed a hand on both our shoulders.

'Do you two want a lift?' It was the dark-haired barman.

Lynn and I stopped and turned to each other. Both our minds shared a single thought. A lift! This meant a car. No one in our family, or Lynn's, had a car. The only time I had been in one was with Mr Popple, after being bullied at school, and after the incident at Club 60, which I had almost blanked out of my mind.

Still in disbelief, we nodded our heads. He hadn't even asked where we lived. I suddenly found my voice.

'Well, if it's no trouble, we wouldn't mind. We don't live far away.'

'Wait here in the doorway. We'll not be long finishing off. What are your names?'

He looked at us in turn.

I'm Jackie and this is Lynn. What's yours?'

'Cliff – and my mate's called John.'

We lit cigs while we waited by the door.

'Do you think they're having us on?' I asked, taking too long a drag on my cigarette, which made me cough and my eyes run, ruining my mascara.

'I don't know, could be, but they seem a bit older than what we're used to, so you could be right. Anyhow, we'll soon find out, they're here now. Wait till we tell the others we got a lift home in a car.'

'You don't think they're too old, do you?' I asked as I finished my cigarette and stamped it out on the floor.

'What's it matter? It's a cold night and a lift beats walking.'

We walked across the car park. The fair-haired lad named John opened the car doors. He was wearing an identical jumper to mine, only a different colour, and his fitted him properly. He wore slim-leg black trousers and polished black shoes. In fact, John and Cliff both looked smart.

The car was big, with a huge bench seat across the front and one in the back.

'What type is it?' I asked, as I slid across the long seat. Lynn sat in the back with Cliff.

'Rover 75,' said John, as he turned the key to start the engine, pressed the start button and switched the heating and lights on.

The smell of leather filled my nose. I gave him directions and he turned left out of the car park. Within minutes, he'd parked outside my house. He switched off the engine.

Curtains twitched and shadows moved across windows at the sound of a car in the street. Cliff pulled out a packet of cigarettes, took one and gave one each to Lynn and me. We lit up.

John didn't smoke. He said no one in their house smoked as asthma ran in the family. I told him bronchitis ran in ours but it didn't stop me and Dad smoking. John went on to say that he was twenty and was the youngest of five. I told him I was the oldest of three and that I had lied to him earlier in the pub – I was only seventeen. He said he already knew.

It went quiet in the back, which was a bit embarrassing. I glanced over my shoulder and Lynn and Cliff had their arms around each other, kissing. I felt John's arm slide across the back of the seat.

'I'm sorry,' I said, pulling away but not wanting to offend. 'I'm just not dating at the moment.' *You'll be returned unopened.* Pete's words came back to me.

'That's all right,' he replied and withdrew his arm. 'Where do you work, Jackie?'

I told him about the chemist and that I was learning the dispensing side.

'What nights are we off next week, John?' Cliff suddenly leaned forward, one arm still around Lynn.

'Tuesday and Thursday,' John said.

'So, girls, do you want to go and see the illuminations next Tuesday night?' Cliff asked.

I turned my head and looked at Lynn. I'd have to do some bribing with Jo, and I didn't want to go as a "date", but neither Lynn nor I had seen the illuminations, yet we'd heard so much about them.

We both agreed that we'd like to go, and we arranged for the lads to pick us up at seven thirty on the following Tuesday.

Lynn and Cliff continued where they had left off. I crushed my cigarette in the ashtray and continued telling John about my job. He opened a window for a few minutes to let the smoke out and to clear the mist-covered back window.

'What about you? Do you work full time behind the bar?'

'No, just part time,' he replied. 'I'm a draftsman; in a drawing office.'

'How interesting. I'm good at drawing – it was my best subject at school. Where do you work?'

'Tinsley Wire, on Sheffield Road.'

My mouth dropped open. I stared at him.

'Never!'

21

'Have you just got out of a car?' Mum asked, as I went into the house.

Dad looked up.

'You stick with him then, if he can afford a car.'

'Dad!' I snapped.

Then Mum started. 'He must have got a good job if he can afford a car. Are you seeing him again?'

'He's a draftsman, listen...'

'Did you say a draftsman? Now that's what you call a good job,' Dad said, and filled his pipe. 'No mucky hands with that job.'

I raised my voice. 'Shut up and listen.' They went quiet. 'He works at the same place as Pete.'

No one spoke, and then Mum looked at me with her all-seeing eyes, that all mothers possess.

'What did he say when you told him about Pete?'

'Nothing. He said he had nothing to do with the pipe-fitters. It was mainly the joiners and brickies he worked with.'

'But he must have said something?'

'He asked if I wanted to talk about it. I said I didn't, and opened the car door and got out.'

'You must be daft. It sounds like you've got a decent bloke there. You hang on to him.'

I became angry. 'You don't know what you're talking about. What do you know about him? Anyway, he's not my type.'

Mum became angry too. 'Think back to what's happened in the

past. You're a fool to yourself, Jack, and not every lad's got Billy Drury and Elvis Presley looks,' she said, as she stormed off to bed.

'It's Fury not Drury, and what do you know about life today?' I shouted after her, but she'd gone. Dad puffed away on his pipe and said nothing.

* * * *

Tuesday morning, and as usual, chaos reigned. All of us getting ready for school or work at the same time, apart from Dad who had left two hours ago.

'You be careful going off to Blackpool tonight,' said Mum as she dashed off to her morning cleaning job. 'I'll have gone to Fletchers before you get in from work.'

'Okay, Mum. I'll see Ian gets to school.' I glared at him. 'Won't I?' I pushed his face into his bowl of Sugar puffs, because he was being cheeky, and was tormenting Shep.

She had come in season and was making her nest in the bottom cupboard, where he kept his football boots. Every time he went near, she had a snap at him. Shep had claimed the bottom of the cupboard as her own special area. We had all moved our shoes and boots elsewhere and placed a piece of old carpet in the bottom of the cupboard. Ian insisted on kicking his boots off in the same place and she didn't like it.

'She'll have you one of these days. You're pushing your luck too far with her.' I said, as he stood by the sink, wiping the sticky puffed wheat off his face and sticking his tongue out at me.

* * * *

No matter how busy it was in the dispensary, I enjoyed it, and today was no exception. I had now learned many of the drugs by name. One of my tasks was to ring through to the wholesalers every morning for replacement supplies of medicines.

I could now mix ointments and pastes, and measure miniscule amounts of powders on the smallest scales I had ever seen: a balance scale with tiny brass weights, some so fine and small that they had to be handled with tweezers. I measured fluids in drops from tiny glass phials.

All the knowledge I had learned at school; weights and measures in pounds and ounces, pints and quarts were of no use in the dispensary, apart from dispensing medicine bottles, which were in ounces. Everything else was metric.

Sometimes I would mix items with a pestle and mortar, and other times on a marble slab with a palette knife, usually with a petroleum jelly base, which I didn't know until now was Vaseline. Sometimes a lanolin base was used. When the paste was thoroughly mixed, I pressed it into jars ranging from one gram to five hundred grams. After making up every prescription, I placed it on the worktop for Mr Fox to check. I took my work in the dispensary very seriously and was fully aware of the implications of doing something wrong.

* * * *

I couldn't wait for the evening to come round, not to see John, but to see the illuminations. When Hazel and I went to Blackpool, it had been during the summer, and the lights weren't on then. Lynn came round at seven for me to apply her make-up, and John and Cliff came at seven thirty. It was dark outside, and curtains across the street moved as the car came down the street.

'How long will it take to get there?' I asked, as Lynn and I stepped into the back of the car.

'About twenty minutes,' John replied.

'It must be a fast car,' I said, remembering the long train ride. Twenty minutes later, John parked up and we got out. Lynn and I looked each other, confused.

'Where are we?' I asked, looking at my surroundings.

'Chapeltown,' Cliff replied. 'Come on, it's not much further.'

208

'Chapeltown? I thought we were going to Blackpool,' I said, as we began walking down the hill. John and Cliff looked at each other and then we all burst out laughing at our ignorance.

'This is Chapeltown – the lights are in the park,' said John. We continued down the hill.

Reaching the entrance, I saw the string of multi-coloured lights hanging above the pathway.

'Haven't you been here before?' asked John, as we walked in pairs along the path.

'No, I've never even heard of it.'

'You see a lot more when you've got a car,' he replied.

He took hold of my hand as we stepped aside to allow a couple with a pram to pass. I removed it after they had gone. We continued around the park and then went to a local pub.

The lads went to the bar while Lynn and I found seats and a table, and then moved, as angry eyes told us we had sat in the wrong place. We found a table next to two old men who were playing dominoes. I again noticed how smartly John dressed, and I liked his professionally cut, neatly combed hairstyle. He returned with a pint for himself and half for me. Cliff followed with similar. They placed the drinks on the table.

I took out a packet of cigarettes and handed them around. John waved his hand.

'Sorry, I forgot you don't smoke.' I noticed his hands: clean, long and slim with trimmed fingernails, and then wondered what he must think of my bitten ones. I drew the hand nearest to him up my sleeve to hide it. We talked for a while as a foursome, learning about each other's jobs and families. Then Cliff suggested more drinks. Lynn and I offered to pay, but the lads refused.

Lynn and Cliff laughed at some private joke. John suggested a run out to Castleton on Sunday afternoon when they had finished work at the pub.

'Yes, if Lynn's going,' I replied. 'How long is it going to take? My mum's going to be in hospital on Thursday.'

'It'll only be for a few hours as we have to be back behind the bar for seven o'clock. The entire bar staff go, in a couple of cars. Have you been to Castleton before?'

I had to laugh.

I thought back to when we were in our early teens and a whole gang of us would go to Castleton in the summer. There were no corridors on the local trains. We made sure we had a carriage to ourselves. The lads would sit on one side of the coach and the girls on the other. We would all be eyeing each other up, taking note of who was sitting where. Then, as we approached Totley tunnel, one of the lads would jump up and pull the central light out. Darkness. There was a scuffle. We screamed and laughed as the lads made a grab for us, had a snog and a crafty feel, only to find that we had all swapped places.

I recalled hearing Dave Hunston shouting at Roy. 'Gerroff, it's me, you daft twat!'

John's voice brought me back to the present. 'What's so funny?' he asked.

'Nothing, sorry,' I replied, the memory fading. 'I've been once or twice, but never in a car.'

The evening passed quickly, and by half past ten, John pulled up outside our house. Lynn and Cliff were kissing in the back, while John and I sat in silence. He suddenly put his hand in his pocket and brought out a packet of Park Drive cigarettes.

'I noticed you smoke these,' he said, and handed them to me.

I didn't know what to say. I hardly knew him. I turned towards him and kissed him on his cheek. It was an instant reaction to receiving a gift.

'Thank you. You shouldn't have,' I said, and looked at the unopened packet of cigarettes in my lap.

He looked at me and smiled.

'You said your Mum's going in hospital on Thursday. That's my night off. Would you like me to take you to see her?'

His dark blue eyes looked almost black with the glow from the street light.

'Thank you, but I couldn't. I don't want to put on you...'

'But you're not putting on me, I'm asking you.'

'No, it would be like a favour, and you'd want something in return.'
John looked shocked.

'No I wouldn't – what makes you think that?'

'Because you're a man, and you're all the same.' I got out of the car, went into the house and slammed the door.

'What's the matter with you?' shouted Mum, as I ran upstairs, crying.

The following night, Mum didn't go into work. I bought a Harmony hair colour from the shop, coloured her hair, and then gave it a trim with some decent scissors bought from Mr Fox. I kept them upstairs in my bedroom drawer. Drying it off with a towel, I coaxed her natural waves into shape with Amami setting lotion, and waited for it to dry. It was so thick, it wouldn't be completely dry until the morning. She covered it with a sleeping net and went to bed.

'That's the best it's looked in years,' she said next morning, and held the hand mirror up to her face in front of the large mirror to see the back view.

She was worried about her forthcoming operation, but was trying bravely not to let it show.

We packed her small suitcase with items of clothing she would need. I added a small tablet of Lux soap in a soapbox, a flannel, towel, denture brush and paste, and a comb, which I placed in a plastic drawstring toiletries bag covered in images of pink roses.

When she wasn't looking, I placed a Max Factor Crème Puff pressed powder compact and Firebrand lipstick in the bottom of the case. I'd bought them as a surprise for when she'd had the operation.

* * * *

I had arranged my hours with Mr Fox, and Audrey at the bottom house was seeing to Ian. After checking Mum in at the hospital, I left for work. She looked ill and old as she waved to me from her bed in the ward. I wished she would pack in some of her cleaning jobs. They made me so annoyed. Rich people who only gave her ten shillings for cleaning their large posh houses, plus their cast-off clothes, which Mum insisted had a value.

'How can they?' I'd argued with her many times. 'You or Dad can't wear any of these – you don't mix in those circles. Why don't you take them to the pawn shop? You might get something for them there!' I snapped.

'They were gifts, and I'll not sell or give away a gift.'

'But can't you see they're only cluttering up your wardrobe. Mum? Sometimes you make me want to scream.'

'It's nothing to do with you. Keep your nose out of my business, and my wardrobe.'

'Well, if you don't tell them you want a pay rise and not their cast offs, I will.'

'You'll do no such thing.' Her colour rose and she clenched her hands.

'Won't I? Watch me!'

I never carried out my threats. After all, it was Mum's life. Perhaps after the operation, her future would be decided by other factors.

* * * *

I returned to work. The shop was busy as usual, as expected at this time of year.

Everyone had chest complaints and the 'flu'. I was also worried about Dad. He too looked ill and old, and still worked full time. He didn't earn much. The company he worked for knew his circumstances. He should have retired years ago but could not, and was willing to accept anything. This was something else that angered me.

At the age of seventy-two, he was giving his all for such little return. I wanted so much to change things, but I knew it was impossible. What could I do about it? The frustrations and unfairness of life started to get to me. Was I growing up or getting old?

It was four o'clock in the afternoon and I was still at work. I knew Audrey was seeing to Ian until Josie and Dad arrived home. I asked Mr Fox if I could use the phone, as I had to phone the hospital after four.

Mum was okay and still in recovery. They told me to phone back at seven, and there would be no visiting tonight.

At five-thirty, Doreen came into the dispensary, saying there was a young man in the shop asking for Jackie. I looked through the peephole and could see John. He was standing at the back of the shop, wearing a suit and tie. I told Mr Fox and Doreen that he was the chap I had been seeing. Mr Fox was well aware of what was happening in my life. He sympathised because I tried my best not to let my home life interfere with work.

'I've no idea what he's doing here,' I said. 'When I last saw him, he offered to take me to the hospital to see Mum, that's all.'

I went into the shop, glanced towards him and smiled as I collected the prescriptions from the coughing and sneezing patients, and took them into the dispensary.

'Those are ready,' said Mr Fox. I noticed the medicines on the corner of the bench, picked them up and walked back into the shop.

'Mr Walters?' I called. A man holding a handkerchief to his nose stepped forward. I placed the items in a pharmacy bag. 'That will be six shillings, please.'

'Good Lord,' he moaned, and fumbled in his pocket. 'What's it coming to?'

'You have three items, Mr Walters,' I said as I took the pound note from him and rung it through the till.

'I should hope I have for that price.' He snatched the change from my hand, then turned and pushed his way through the crowded shop towards the door.

John was still standing at the back of the shop. I beckoned him towards the corner.

'What are you doing here?' I whispered.

'I thought you were going to the hospital.'

He had come straight from work. I looked towards the back of the counter and could see Mr Fox peering through the peephole.

'There's no need, John,' I said. 'They're not allowing visitors tonight.'

'Is she all right?' he asked.

'She's comfortable, that's all they told me.' I looked around at the anxious customers. 'Look, I'm sorry but I can't talk.'

He smiled. 'I'll be waiting outside.'

I was tired when the last customer left the shop. I phoned the hospital again. Everything was all right. It had been a long day, and evening.

'Goodnight,' I called to Mr Fox as I left the shop, and he began switching off the lights. 'See you tomorrow.'

I wrapped my scarf around my neck and pulled on my gloves. John was sitting in the car. My feet and legs were aching, and I was more than glad of the lift.

'So there's no visiting tonight?' he asked, as I bent down to enter the warmth.

'No, they told me to phone in the morning.'

'If you don't have to go to the hospital, why don't we call for some fish and chips, or a drink?' he said, as he started the car.

I thought of home and wondered whether Ian, Dad and Josie had eaten any tea. I looked at my watch. Seven-thirty.

'Anywhere,' I said, as I slumped onto the soft leather seat.

22

Sitting in the Old Vic having a drink, a pickled egg and a packet of crisps, I apologized for my outburst the other night, and thought it only fair to tell him about Pete.

'John, I think you ought to know something. I enjoy your company and your thoughtfulness but I can't let it go any further. I've been hurt and don't want it to happen again.'

'Is this to do with that Pete chap you mentioned the other night?'

I nodded and looked down at my bitten nails. No point in hiding them now.

'Yes, it's all to do with him. I was madly in love with him and we were getting engaged at Christmas.'

I stopped and bit my lip as thoughts of that awful evening came back to me.

He leaned towards me. 'Go on…'

* * * *

'Sit down, love, there's something I have to tell you'. Mum's face was grave and the tone of her voice stilled me. It was like the time she had told me about the brooch, all those years ago.

I sat down slowly.

She took a deep breath. 'It's about Pete.'

'What about Pete?' The words couldn't come out fast enough.

'He's seeing someone else,' she said. 'He's engaged to her.'

I felt the colour drain from my face. I stood up. There must be some mistake. How could Mum possibly know anything like that?

'It's true, love.' Mum saw my entire future slipping away and placed her arms around me. I stood still, in shock, then removed her arms and sat back down.

'I didn't want to tell you, but I knew I must. You're my daughter. I thought at first that he might be finishing with this other girl now he's met you. But he's not. He's going away with her family for Christmas, to Bournemouth.'

She stroked my hair, while she spoke.

'It has to be a mistake – we're getting engaged at Christmas…besides, no one from up North goes to Bournemouth.' I was still refusing to believe it, but I knew my mother would never lie or joke about something like this. I sat thinking for a few minutes, while Mum put the kettle on.

'How do you know this, Mum?' I didn't know whether to cry or scream.

She filled the teapot.

'Her mother told me.'

* * * *

John listened patiently while I told him. At one point, he took hold of my hand. I pulled it away.

'What happened then?' he asked, and took a drink from his glass.

I lit a cigarette, and continued.

'He came to our house later that same evening, after Mum had gone to work. I was ready – make-up on, coat and gloves. My stomach was twisting in knots and I was dreading the confrontation.'

* * * *

'Hello, Charlie,' he said to Dad. 'How's things? Still smoking that old pipe, I see.' He wafted away the thick smoke coming from Dad's pipe.

Shep barked, trotted up to him and sniffed. Satisfied, she returned to her cupboard.

'What's the homework, Jo?' He patted her shoulder.

She gave him a sullen look. 'Nuclear Physics,' she replied, tossing her head back and taking herself and books upstairs. 'There's no peace anywhere in this place,' she mumbled as she left.

I watched his every move. He was no different than when I had last seen him. Mum had to be mistaken. Deep down, I knew she couldn't be.

'Howdy pard'ner,' he said to Ian, and drew an imaginary gun from his pocket. 'Bang! Bang!'

Ian immediately dropped to the floor and rolled under the table, then sneaked out the other side and crept up on Pete, grabbing him round his legs.

'Come on, let's go,' I said, not wanting to delay this any longer. 'I don't feel like going to the pictures tonight, Pete,' I said, as we walked down our entry.

'What do you want to do then?' he asked, sliding his arm around me.

Yesterday, I would have leaned my head against his shoulder. Today, I just froze.

'Let's go for a walk instead.'

He stopped. 'A walk? It's freezing.'

I turned to him. 'I'm sure we'll find somewhere we can get warmed up,' and forced a smile.

We walked until there was no one else around. By the top side of the park, I stopped and turned to face him. My heart jumped into my mouth.

'Pete. Who's Carol?'

* * * *

I took a drink of my beer and lit a cigarette. I was about to continue when a man came over and sat down at our table.

'Ey up, Johnny boy, what are you doin' down here? Come for some fresh air, 'av you?' He laughed, glanced at me, smiled and looked back at John, giving a wink of approval.

'Just having a change,' John replied, then introduced me. 'Jackie has just finished work, so I thought we'd have a pint before supper.'

'Busman's holiday, eh? Can I get you two a drink?'

'No thanks,' I shook my head.

'We're okay just now, thanks Ken,' said John. 'We're going for some fish and chips after this one.' John turned to me as Ken walked away. 'What happened next?'

I finished my drink. My melancholy mood had evaporated.

'I'll tell you later. Come on, let's get some chips, I'm starving.'

* * * *

We stood outside the chip shop, eating our fish and chips. There were too many people passing by to carry on our conversation.

When we had finished, John pulled a clean white hanky from his pocket and handed it to me. I wiped my hands and passed it back for John to wipe his. We made our way back to the car. The heater soon warmed us through and I was almost asleep as we pulled up outside our house.

'Are you going to finish what you were saying?' he asked. He turned off the engine, but left the heater running.

My thoughts turned again to that terrible night as I looked at John, his face full of concern.

'He didn't have to say anything. His face said it all. I felt as if a rocket had shot off inside me.' I had just stood there, staring at him. My world had shattered in seconds. Anger, betrayal, hatred, murder. 'I wanted to stab him a thousand times. If I'd been carrying a knife, I would have.'

'Didn't he say anything?'

I looked straight into John's blue eyes.

'Yes. Pete hung his head, and said he was sorry.'

* * * *

'So it is true then?' I turned to walk away, my body trembling. I was walking away from someone I loved with all my heart, and couldn't go through with it. I turned back to him.

'Why, Pete, why?'

He was standing away from me, his hands in his pockets, looking down at his shoes. 'You know why,' he said quietly.

Then it hit me, and it fuelled my anger.

'Because I wouldn't have sex with you, that's it, isn't it? You rotten bastard,' I shouted. 'You wouldn't use anything or I would have done. I didn't want to get pregnant.'

'What difference would it make?' he shouted back. 'You'd be getting pregnant sooner or later.'

I saw a side to him I'd never seen before; his face ugly, contorted, sneering.

'You're so, so wrong, Pete Mathers. I will never get pregnant outside marriage. I would never let my parents down. They have so much trust in me. I will always do what's right by them, and would never bring them any disgrace.'

I turned and began to run.

'If that's what you think, you'll have a long wait,' he shouted. 'You know what'll happen to you when you go to your maker. You'll be stamped, Returned – Unopened.'

* * * *

'And that's the last I saw or heard of him.'

I looked down at my lap. John was holding my hand. This time I didn't move it.

23

I didn't see John the following night as he was working.

Dad and I took Jo and Ian to see Mum in hospital. We were early and could see her through the round glass panels in the doors. She was sitting up in bed, wearing her new bed jacket with pink roses dotted all over it. Her eyes were fixed on the doors.

Ian rushed through first, thrusting the flowers at her, and promptly asked her when she was coming home, as he wanted a homemade meat and potato pie. We gave her a gentle hug.

The nurse came over.

'Only two persons at a time, please.'

Jo and I left and waited outside in the corridor. An old woman sat in a chair near the door. She coughed, which sounded like a death rattle. I wondered why she was outside a ward and not in one.

'When will we know if it's Cancer?' Jo asked, wiping her nose.

'I don't know, Mum never said. She just said they would take away what was necessary.' The hysterectomy was a matter of routine and a precaution. At her age, she was unlikely to have any more pregnancies.

'We'll ask her when we go in,' said Jo.

We stood in silence for a few minutes, leaning against the opposite walls of the corridor. I didn't see much of Jo now, even though we lived in the same house. She was always doing homework and I was always busy doing something else.

I looked across at her, twelve years old, a Grammar School student, her sandy blonde hair still wild and unruly; Cliff Richard's number one fan.

'How's school going?' I asked.

'It's all right. Much more work to do, but I enjoy it.'

'Have you made any new friends?'

'No, not really,' she replied. 'Different class of people to the ones who live in our area.'

I had noticed she hadn't been seeing much of Ann from across the street recently. I suppose that was understandable; they didn't go to the same school any more.

She was quiet, leaning against the wall, examining her fingernails.

'I know you're not my real sister.'

My heart skipped a beat. There was an unbearable long silence, as I didn't know how to reply. I looked straight across at her. She was still staring at her fingernails. I had always thought I would be the one to tell her. I never thought it would be like this, in a hospital corridor.

'How long have you known?'

She shrugged her shoulders and slowly lifted her head.

'A few weeks.' She yawned and peered through the glass panel.

I knew Mum and Dad wouldn't have told her.

'Ann told me,' she said, and leaned back against the wall.

'Does it bother you?'

She looked across at me.

'No, should it?'

I was still shocked over her complacency. Why didn't she want to know more?

Ian suddenly came bursting through the doors eating a banana, a big grin across his face.

'Where have you got that from?' I asked.

'Woman in next bed to Mum gave it to me, said she didn't want it.'

'I hope you thanked her for it.'

'I did, and I asked if she'd got any sweets she didn't want.'

Jo and I looked at each other for a moment and then laughed. Nothing had changed.

'You cheeky devil,' I said.

He grinned again. He looked so funny with no teeth. His second set was only just starting to come through.

'She showed me her scar with a plaster over it,' he added, as he pushed the rest of the banana into his mouth.

'Who did, the woman in the next bed?' said Jo, examining her fingernails again.

Ian laughed and shook his head.

'I've seen her scar with stitches…' he tried to whisper. He couldn't speak for giggling. 'And she's got stubby ginger hairs.' He looked around to see if anyone was listening and burst out laughing.

Dad came through the doors. I found him a chair. He couldn't stand for long periods as it gave him dizzy spells.

Jo and I entered the ward. Mum was worried about how we were coping.

'I hope they let me out soon.' She winced as she tried to shift her position.

'Ian's been telling us about your scar,' I told her.

'And the Technicolor hair,' Jo added. 'In fact, everyone in the corridor knows.' Jo's face was poker straight.

'The little monkey – just wait 'til I see him again,' Mum said, grimacing, as another pain shot through her.

* * * *

Apart from the seriousness of Mum's operation, and the fact that Jo now knew we were stepsisters and didn't make an issue out of it, I was feeling much better in myself than I had for a long time.

I was pleased that I had made an effort and gone out with Lynn and the others on Christine's birthday. We did have a good time. Fun had been seriously lacking in my life recently. I was also glad I had met John. He was a nice lad, not a bit selfish, and was softly-spoken and gentle in his manner. He didn't have film star looks, but he was tall, slim and well-groomed. He was always clean-shaven, with neatly cut and combed hair. And he had a car! He looked so at ease behind the wheel; confident. Perhaps because he was older than most of the lads I knew, apart from the milkman of course.

* * * *

Before I left John on Thursday night, I had agreed to let him take us all to the hospital on Sunday afternoon instead of the proposed outing to Castleton.

Ian and Jo were looking forward to a ride in the car, even Dad was, but today his chest, which had been bothering him all week, was no better. I finished work at one o'clock as it was Saturday, and when I arrived home, Dad had a high temperature. I made him some onion broth and told him to go to bed for the afternoon.

'I'll be back around six,' I said. 'I'm taking Jo and Ian to see Mum and then we're going into town. Take some more Gee's Linctus at five o'clock.' I kissed him on the cheek.

'Give my love to your mother,' he whispered in a hoarse voice.

'I will. You get some sleep and I'll see you later.'

Jo and Ian were ready and waiting downstairs.

'Have you taken Shep for a wee?' I asked, as I pulled my coat on. They stood, looking like a couple of garden gnomes.

'Never mind, I'll do it.' I stormed past them. 'Come on, Shep,' I took her into the yard where she quickly squatted. 'I'll take you for a proper walk when I come back.' I tickled her ears and stroked her head as she followed me back inside.

'Come on, you two cloth heads.'

* * * *

Mum was doing fine; she had no results yet, apart from the doctor being quite pleased with her progress. We spent over an hour with Mum, only leaving when forced to by the matron. Mum cried as we left, and she wasn't the only one, as I looked around at the other women in the ward saying goodbye to their families.

We took the bus into town and went straight to Woolworths. I wanted to buy Jimmy Crawford's new record, *I Love How You Love Me*. I'd heard it on the radio and couldn't wait to get my own copy. I bought Jo a magazine featuring Cliff Richard. I couldn't see what she saw in him; too baby-faced for my liking. I told her she would be more entertained if she listened to Little Richard instead of Cliff Richard, but she didn't want to know about an "old has-been".

Ian had been hankering all week for an Airfix fighter plane kit to assemble, and he decided on a Spitfire.

'That'll be much too difficult for you,' I said, as I handed a two-shilling piece over the counter.

'You'll make it for me, Jack, won't you?' He grinned cheekily.

He'd started buying Airfix kits with his pocket money. He couldn't assemble any of them, but would sit for hours, his chin resting on his fists, elbows on the table while I fastened the delicate structures together. Then he would go and show his pals what he had made!

The following morning after breakfast, I went upstairs to change the bedding. John was taking us to the hospital at half past two. Dad sat breathing heavily in the bedside chair while I checked the poultice on his chest, changed the candy-striped cotton sheets and pillowcases, then went downstairs to refill the hot water bottle. I helped him back into bed and closed the bedroom door behind me as I left.

I changed Jo and Ian's beds in the back bedroom, and then mine, after putting my new record on repeat play. *I love how you love me...* I was singing along to it when Ian came running upstairs.

'Jack-Jack, a man's just come down our street on a Royal Enfield and he's parked outside our house.'

I was only half-listening to him as I was concentrating on the song. 'I love how you loooooovvvee mee...' I sang to Ian as he came nearer, waved a pillow case in his face and fluttered my eyelashes. Embarrassed, he rushed towards me and grabbed my hand.

'Jack, listen, it's someone outside our house.' Ian pulled me towards the stairs. 'Come on, hurry.'

I went downstairs and gasped when I looked out of the front

window. John was standing astride a motor bike. Some of the young lads who lived in the street were gathered around him in awe.

'Come on, Jack, do you know him?' Ian said as he pulled me out of the back door and down the entry.

I stood, staring. The only bikers I'd seen were always dressed in black leathers and boots. John was dressed in slim leg black trousers, black pointed-toe shoes, a black open-neck shirt and a blue sports jacket. Somehow, he looked taller and quite handsome. At that moment, his hair flopped over his forehead and he looked the double of James Dean. He gently flicked it back while speaking to the lads who were admiring the bike. Even old Mr Clarke and Mr Ford were giving their appraisal, and reminiscing about the bikes they'd had before the War. Ian pulled me towards him.

John smiled when he saw me.

'Jack…' Ian tugged my hand. I tugged it back and looked down at the little pest.

'Hello, John, this is my nuisance of a brother, Ian.'

Ian let go of my hand and rushed over to him, his eyes fixed on the bike.

'John, can I have a ride on it?

I suddenly became aware of what a mess I looked, and pulled Mum's pinny over my head.

'How is your mum?' John asked.

'I don't know, I've been too busy to ring this morning,' I replied, still mesmerised.

'Nice bike, Mister.' Greg Batten, one of Ian's friends joined the small crowd.

'It's my sister's boyfriend's bike, and I'm going a ride on it.'

I felt the colour rise in my cheeks.

'Ian!' I snapped.

Jo appeared by my side, clutching her workbook to her chest, a sullen look on her face, as usual.

'Look at this, Jo! I'm going a ride on it.' Ian was at it again.

Jo looked at the bike and then its owner, analysed him and looked back at the bike.

'It's all right, I suppose. With or without an engine, it's still a cycle.' She turned, sulking, back down the entry.

'Have you sold your car?' I moved nearer. The engine ticked as it cooled.

'Heck, no. That's why I've got the two jobs – to pay for the upkeep.' He smiled and winked.

'Come on, John...' Ian pestered.

'Can he?' John and Ian looked at me.

How could I refuse? Mum would have a fit if she was here. She wouldn't allow Jo or me to have a push bike. When she was younger, Jo had owned a Mobo Safety Bike with stabilisers, but Mum wouldn't allow her to take it out of the yard. But there would be no stopping Ian when he got older.

I looked at John's face and then at Ian's.

'Go on then.'

Ian's face lit up like a beacon. John straddled the bike, rocked it forward to raise the stand and pressed down heavily with his right foot. He seated himself as the bike roared into life, filling the street with noise and the smell of petrol. I helped Ian onto the back.

'Hold on tight,' said John, as he looked over his shoulder to see if Ian was firmly in place.

Ian placed his arms as far as he could around John's waist. He turned his head towards me, his blue eyes full of excitement as they rode out of the street. I suddenly thought of Dad lying ill upstairs, too old to get involved with sports and pastimes with his only son. They had both missed something.

* * * *

'Can I have a go, mister?'

John was bombarded with youngsters when he returned. Some had even come from the next street.

'Only if your parents say so,' he said, as Ian, climbed reluctantly off

226

the back of the bike.

Half an hour later, all the kids had been for a ride.

'Where did you take them?' I asked.

'Not far – up Parkside Road, on Middlewood Road and down Leppings Lane,' he replied. 'Your turn now.' His hair fell forward over his eyes as he tilted the bike to one side for me. He flicked it back, waiting. A butterfly awoke in my chest.

I daren't. Mum would go mad if she knew. The temptation was too strong. What the heck! I threw the pinny at Ian.

'Here, hang on to that.'

'Tuck your skirt in,' John said as I climbed on the back. 'Hang on.' He looked back.

I placed my arms around his waist. It felt strange holding someone else again.

John slipped it into gear and roared out of the street, but instead of going across and up the road where he had taken the boys, he turned right, weaving in and out of the traffic along Penistone Road, past my old school, leaving the rows of houses behind, and out into the countryside.

As he picked up speed, I held on tightly, peering over his shoulder as the wind whipped my hair around my face. '*I'm only halfway to Paradise…*' I could hear the voice of Billy Fury as we sped into hills of Derbyshire.

* * * *

I was freezing cold and my beehive hairstyle looked like an abandoned stork's nest as we arrived back and John pulled up outside the house.

Ian was alone, crying as he ran down the entry. I almost fell off the bike in my rush to comfort him.

'What's the matter?' I asked, as I pulled him towards me.

He put his arms around me.

'It's Dad. He's dead.' He rubbed his eyes. 'When's Mum coming home?'

24

Shep rushed out of her cupboard as I dashed into the house.

'Dad! Dad!' I called, as I ran upstairs and into his bedroom.

His arm was hanging out of the bed and his face was grey. He had slid down the bed instead of being propped up on the pillows.

He was breathing slightly. I tapped his face and his shoulder.

'He's not dead,' I said to a white-faced Ian. 'Go and find Jo. Dad, wake up. Dad.'

'Can I help?' It was John. I had forgotten about him. He was standing by the bedroom door.

'Please, if you don't mind. I'm sorry about this, but can you help me to get him back up the bed? Dad, this is John, he's a friend of mine.'

Dad didn't reply. He just nodded his acknowledgement, as we held him under his armpits and lifted him back up the bed.

Jo appeared.

'What's happened?' She looked on as John and I raised Dad back up the bed.

'He's took a turn for the worse. Can you go and phone the doctor? There are some coins in my purse downstairs.' I suddenly remembered her condition. 'And don't run,' I added.

'Do you want me to do anything, Jack?' Ian asked. He had been watching from the foot of the bed.

'Yes, you can take those dirty sheets off the landing downstairs for me, please, and don't trip over them.'

I looked at John and felt embarrassed. Dad in this state, my hair still uncombed. I looked away.

'I'm sorry, John,' was all I could say.

'Look, I hate to leave you like this but I've got to go to work – we open at twelve, and the customers will hammer the door down if we're not on time.'

'That's okay. I'm more than grateful for what you've done.' I stroked Dad's hand.

'I'll be back around two thirty – I'll come in the car as planned, if that's okay.'

'Thanks,' I nodded. 'Will you see yourself out? And watch out for Shep, she's a tendency to nip when someone's leaving.'

A few minutes later, I heard the sound of John's bike as it growled up the street, along the main road and into the distance.

I looked at Dad and began to cry. I was supposed to be looking after him. What if he had died while I was riding around on the back of a motorbike in Derbyshire? Mum would never forgive me or trust me again. Then I remembered Ian's face as he'd sat on the back of the bike, and John, someone I hardly knew, who had seen me at my worst, and how he'd helped with Dad. Choked by tears, I knew that whatever the future held, somehow, John would always be there for me.

* * * *

'It's pneumonia,' the doctor said. 'And quite possibly double. I think both lungs are affected.' He placed his stethoscope and notes back in his bag. He wasn't our usual doctor; he was an out-of-hours locum. He looked at me, Josie and then Ian.

'Is he going to die?' Ian asked, a worried frown on his face. I pulled him towards me and cuddled him.

'Of course he isn't,' snapped Jo, as she sat on the bed, sobbing.

'I don't think so.' The doctor fastened his bag and looked at Ian. 'Provided we get your granddad into hospital straight away.'

'He's not my granddad, he's my dad.'

The doctor looked at the three of us.

'Where's your mother?'

'In hospital,' I replied.

* * * *

Somehow, with the help of Auntie Doris, Audrey and my dear boss, we managed to get through the following weeks. Mum and Dad were out of hospital for Christmas, although it wasn't much of one, again. We were all too tired to put much effort into it, but we decorated the tree with baubles and hung the trimmings around the walls. We were grateful to be together, and enjoyed what we had.

John became a family favourite and I began seeing him more often, and missed him when he wasn't around. He bought me a Ladies' Colibri cigarette lighter for Christmas; it was smaller than the normal ones. John's mum wanted me to come for Christmas dinner, but when John explained about our family dramas, she understood why I had declined.

* * * *

Lynn and Cliff drifted apart and shortly afterwards, she met another lad called Alan. It wasn't long before they became serious about each other.

I became more involved with John. On Sunday afternoons, he took me to places I had never been to before: Matlock, Matlock Bath, Buxton, Bakewell, Darley Dale, and not just me: he took Jo, Ian, Shep, and sometimes Mum and Dad. They felt so proud, sitting in the car and being taken to places they had never seen either. What a difference having a car made.

* * * *

Our friendship gradually changed into something more, and our first kiss was in the car. How different it was to standing in draughty

230

entries! It was John's night off, and after we'd visited a few pubs, we shared fish and chips and drove to a lay-by. He put his arm around my neck and I nuzzled closer. He put his other arm around me. I felt safe, warm and loved.

'Come on, let's get in the back,' he said, removing his jacket.

We moved into the back of the car where there was more room. He slid towards me and held me in his arms. I raised my head and his lips were on mine, soft and gentle while holding me close. I hadn't been kissed since Pete and couldn't help but compare them.

Pete's kisses had been strong, forceful and filled me with a passion I had sometimes feared.

John pulled away slightly. 'Are you all right?' he asked, concerned.

I nodded, and pulled him towards me. He came closer as I slid further down the shiny leather seat. We kissed again, this time with more passion. He kissed my neck and the base of my throat, and his hand slowly unfastened the buttons on my blouse. He held back slightly, waiting for my reaction, and then slid his hand beneath my bra. This felt different. I didn't stop him. I helped him by releasing the front straps and opening my blouse fully. He kissed and stroked my breasts and I felt warm inside.

I lay flat on the seat and his hand slid up my skirt and stroked the top of my legs and stockings, running his hand over and under my suspenders while covering my lips with his. His fingers slowly slid into the edge of my panties. I opened my legs and then froze. I pushed him off and pulled myself up.

'What's the matter?' he said, panting.

'Nothing, I'm sorry.' With shaking hands, keeping my head bowed, I fastened my bra and blouse. Even though it was semi-dark, I couldn't bear to look at him.

He got out of the car and tidied himself, then came round and opened the door for me.

'I'm sorry, John,' I said, looking straight ahead as I got out and slid onto the front seat. He closed the car door and went around to the other side, and started the engine.

231

'There's no need to apologise, it was my fault I got carried away.'

Winding down the window to clear the steam, he pulled out of the lay-by and turned for home. We didn't speak and I was glad when we arrived. I've lost him, I thought as he braked. I opened the car door.

'What's the rush?' he said, and switched off the engine. He moved towards me. 'When are we seeing each other again, or don't you want to?'

'Are you sure you want to?' I said, and reached over to him. 'I didn't think you'd want to after – you know...'

'Come here, silly.' He pulled me into his arms. 'What – and miss taking you and your family out on Sunday afternoons? Not likely!' His blue eyes twinkled.

* * * *

For Valentine's Day, John gave me a slim white cardboard box. Inside it was a heart-shaped card made of white satin and covered in red roses, with a red lace surround. Written across the top in gilt, it said: *To the One I Love. This Special Card is sent your way to wish you a Happy Valentine's Day,* and signed, *With Love, John.*

He took me home to meet his family. I couldn't wait, especially as he'd told me they had an inside toilet and a bathroom upstairs. Although John was the youngest, he still had two brothers and a sister living at home, and another sister who was married with a baby and lived nearby. It was Sunday afternoon and all his family was waiting to meet me. I was quite nervous, and lit a cigarette as soon as I arrived.

I stood in the back garden. It was dominated by an old air-raid shelter built of bricks with a roof of rounded sheets of corrugated iron.

I turned around as John's mother came out to greet me.

'This is Mum,' said John, smiling. 'Mum, meet Jackie.'

I was shocked. She was old and frail, her body broken and bent. She reminded me of Granddad. Her hair, thick silver-grey, was cropped straight across just below her ears and held back with two hairgrips. She wore a long black skirt with a faded blouse and hand-knitted grey cardigan. Most of her body was covered with an empire style pinafore. She wore plaid pom-pom carpet slippers on her distorted feet. She looked up at me with a face etched with pain and then took hold of my hand to lead me into her home.

We entered by the back door. There was a door to the right leading to the toilet. The door straight ahead was to the coal store; they didn't have cellars. The door on the left led into a small kitchen, half the size of ours at home. A set-pot was in the corner, along with a washing tub and a large mangle with wooden rollers.

She led me through into the front room, which was quite large. The first thing that caught my eye wasn't John's family, waiting to greet me. It was the huge Yorkshire Range and the large pegged rug on the lino-covered floor.

'Welcome, Jackie. Please sit down.' Her clouded brown eyes smiled warmly. John's mum was still holding my hand as she pointed to an old leather armchair, covered with crocheted covers and plump cushions in embroidered cases. I finished my cigarette, threw it into the fire, and sat down. Her voice was soft and quiet, as if every word spoken was an effort.

'I'll just get some tea. Do you take milk and sugar, Jackie?' She withdrew her small gnarled hand.

'Yes please. Two sugars.' She hobbled away into the kitchen. John introduced his dad, Harry, and his two brothers, Tom and Harry.

'Why didn't they call you Dick?' I said and looked at John. He and his brothers laughed

'And these are my sisters, Mary and Annie.' Mary looked ill. She was having difficulty breathing. The toddler she was nursing was restless. Her older sister Annie took the child into the kitchen. They all made me feel very welcome, asking where I worked and what I did. Mary gasped for breath after every word. John told me later that Mary had severe asthma, emphysema and COPD, and that he'd too had asthma as a child.

John's Mum returned with a tray full of tea, and a chocolate cake cut into wedges. She handed me a china cup and saucer and placed a piece of cake on a matching plate. I looked around and felt the odd one out. Only I had a china cup.

'I have to leave now, Jackie, I'm seeing a friend. It's been lovely meeting you,' said Annie and kissed her mother on the cheek as she left.

The afternoon went well and then John's mum, Mabel, made salad for tea, with cold roast beef from the Sunday joint. I went into the kitchen to help, but she told me she could manage.

'I'll carry the plates in for you then,' I said and watched as she sliced thin slices off the beef and trimmed all the fat before putting it on a plate. I looked at the other plates of untrimmed meat and salad.

'That's our John's' she said and handed me the plate. 'He doesn't like fat.'

'Neither do I – are these anyone's?' I asked, pointing to the other plates already set out. I carried the plates through to the front room. Mabel followed.

'Sit down, love.' She placed a plate in front of me. I looked down at the meat, trimmed of fat.

John and I sat at the table with Mary, while John's brothers and dad sat in chairs and on the settee. His mum didn't sit down at all.

'Let me help,' I offered, but she wouldn't hear of it. She waited on us all, as if it was her duty. I felt humbled at this frail, ill woman, who worked so hard for her grown-up family. I tried to imagine my mum looking after us like this. Never!

* * * *

John and I left at quarter to seven, as he had to be at the pub for opening time. I sat on one of the high stools at the front of the bar. It was quiet early on, so John paid for a drink and placed it in front of me. I lit a cigarette.

I was deep in thought.

'Why does your mum look after you all like that? She's an ill woman.'

'Jack,' he replied. It was the first time he had called me Jack. Frustration showed in his face. 'She won't stop. We've all told her. You saw the cooker in the kitchen – it's brand new, but she won't use it. She insists it doesn't cook as good as the fire oven.'

'But she's got such a hard life. How old is she?'

'Almost sixty, I think.'

I thought of the difference in our mothers. John served a customer and came back to me.

'Why is she so poorly?' I asked.

'I don't know for sure – some problem women have. She had an operation a few years ago and she's never been the same since.' He went to serve another customer. I thought of Mum and her recent operation.

I couldn't sleep that night. I tossed and turned, thinking about how such a kind and loving woman could suffer so much. I told Mum about her next morning.

'I don't know how she copes with all that lot at home and only one married,' Mum said as she buttered a slice of toast and passed it to Ian, who was looking in a mirror and seeing how many Sugar Puffs he could stick in his hair. 'Stop playing with your food, Ian,' she said and then turned back to me. 'That's probably why she took to you, love, to get him married off – one less to look after.'

25

One night on John's evening off, we were sitting in the Blue Ball.

'The lads are going to Cadwell Park and staying over next weekend. Would you mind if I went with them?' he asked.

I looked at him. The colour rose in my face.

'What's happening at Cadwell?' I lit a cigarette. My hands were shaking. I was angry.

'Bike racing – we go every year.'

Not this year you don't, I wanted to say. I stayed silent, and then my thoughts turned to words.

'But what about the pub? You can't have time off over the weekend.'

'Doug and Elsie don't mind – they know I go every year.' He took a drink of his beer.

I was still seething.

'But where will you stay?'

'Tents or car, it doesn't really matter. We usually stay in the bar overnight.'

'Do girls go?' I was trying to sound like I didn't care.

'Yes, and some even ride bikes. Last year one girl had a Harley, it was a...'

'I'm just going to the back.' I said without looking at him. I slid out of my seat, grabbed my handbag and went to the toilet. Girls with motor bikes, I grumbled to myself. I couldn't even ride a push bike.

I reapplied my lipstick and went back into the bar. I didn't go over to him straight away. I went to the jukebox, found a shilling in my purse and placed it into the slot.

I sat back down as my selected disc began to play.

The plaintive chords and ghostly backing vocals started, before the galloping rhythm. John Leyton's voice filled the room…

'If you don't want me to go, just say and I'll stay.' John took hold of my hand.

'No, you go, I wouldn't dream of trying to stop you.' Liar.

'Besides, I think it's next weekend when Doreen at work is having a birthday party down town.' Why on earth did I say that? The only parties Doreen went to were funeral parties.

'That'll be great then. I'm glad you'll have somewhere to go. Better than sitting at the bar waiting for me on Saturday nights, eh? Do you want another beer?' He got up to go to the bar.

Johnny, remember me…' John Leyton sang.

* * * *

The weekend came. How could he go, and leave me here? It was the most miserable weekend of my life. I couldn't sleep. I and tossed and turned all Saturday night, then went for a five-mile walk with Shep the following morning.

By Sunday afternoon, I had convinced myself to never see him again. If he thought I was going up to the pub on Monday night, he had better think again. And if he came to the shop looking for me, I would tell Mr Fox and Doreen to tell him I'd left. There were plenty more fish in the sea. I'd show him – I'd find a new bloke and take him up to the pub when John was working.

I had stopped biting my nails for three weeks and then bit them off in one afternoon.

'What on earth's the matter with you?' said Mum while she was doing the ironing and listening to *Sing Something Simple* on the wireless. 'You've been in a bad mood all weekend.'

'You know why, so why are you asking?' I slumped over a chair, half in it, half out.

'Give the lad a break – he's got every right to go out with his pals. Here, take this pile of repairs if you want something to do.' She pointed to a small pile of clothes on the corner of the table.

'What are you staring at? That's an improvement, anyhow,' I said to Ian, who had distorted his face by pulling a nylon stocking over his head. I pulled it down further. 'There, you'll stop like it now.' He panicked as he tried to pull it off, and I held on to the bottom.

'Maaam!' he started to yell.

'Let go of him,' said Mum, as she banged down the iron.

I let go of the stocking. Ian thumped me in the back as he dragged the stocking off his head and ran away.

I looked back at Mum, who was now holding out the pile of repairs.

'I'm not doing them. Get "Brains" upstairs to do them – she's not doing her homework, she's only reading a magazine.' Mum's eyes darkened.

'Okay, give them here,' I said. 'I'll take them up to her.'

I went upstairs, where Jo was busy with her homework.

'Here, Jo. Mum says you have to do these – she reckons it's time you learned how to use the sewing machine.'

'What time have I got? I haven't finished my homework yet and I'm back at school tomorrow.'

'Oh! What a shame. You should have started your homework earlier then.' I placed the clothes on the bed.

'I'm not doing them. You do the mundane tasks.' She tossed her hair back and looked down at her homework. I was just going to pull the book away from her when I heard Shep bark.

'Jack!' Mum called upstairs.

'Whaaaat?' I shouted back.

'It's someone for you.'

'I'm not in.' I went to the top of the stairs and listened.

'She's upstairs with Jo.' I heard her say. I crept down a few steps to hear better, then the door opened and John appeared.

'John,' I cried. 'What are you doing here? I flew down the rest of the stairs and into his arms.

238

'I came back early. I couldn't go a whole weekend without seeing you.'

* * * *

I was sitting by the bar in the pub's lounge one night. The concert room wasn't open midweek, so there was no entertainment. The taproom was full of regular drinkers who smoked heavily, and played darts, dominoes and cards.

'I'm leaving the pub,' he said, as the bar area dropped quiet for a while.

I was shocked. 'Why?'

'So we can spend more time together. I miss you when I don't see you.'

'Me too. I wish I could see you every night, like Lynn and Alan see each other.'

'That's what I mean, but I can't leave for another few months as I still owe our Harry for the bike. I could sell it, I suppose.'

'But I don't mind sitting at the bar some nights. Besides, I still have my wallpapering jobs on the other nights.'

'It doesn't seem right though, you sitting here, waiting.'

The landlady, Elsie must have overhead. She came towards me.

'Why don't you come and work behind the bar with John? We could do with an attractive girl like you here.'

John and I glanced at each other.

I can't, Elsie. I'm not old enough! I couldn't tell her that.

'I'd love to, Elsie, but I can't. I have to work late some nights. I'm learning the dispensing side, but when I've finished my training I will, if you'll still have me.' I spoke to her with more confidence than I was feeling.

'There will always be a job for a good-looking girl like you, Jackie. Let me know when you're available. What are you having, love? Half of bitter, is it?'

John stood behind her, relieved. Elsie pulled a glass of bitter and placed it in front of me.

'Cheers, Elsie,' I said, and lit a cigarette.

* * * *

We were in love and couldn't get enough of each other. However, we had a problem with having sex. Not with the act itself – it was more that family members always got in the way of it. Someone was always in his house, and the same in mine. Plus the fact that John worked five evenings of each week, meant we had very little time together alone. Waiting for my parents to go to bed so we could have the settee added up to too many late nights and did not fit in with early rising for a day's work.

Lynn and I had talked about it often enough with friends, about where and when it would happen the first time, how would we feel and what if we got pregnant. I spoke to Auntie Doris about what it was like to have sex.

'It's not all it's cocked up to be,' she had said, laughing at her own joke.

'That's our Doris…vulgar as ever,' Mum said when I told her, and then she admitted there were no choirs of angels or brass bands playing when it happened to her.

Lynn and Alan were doing it, and so were Hazel and Mick. After the disastrous first attempt in the lay-by, I was now ready and wanting to experience what almost everyone raved about.

* * * *

The first time was after Mum and Dad had gone to bed one night. I turned the television off, left the small side lamp on and lay on the settee with John. We kissed, gently at first and then with so much passion we rolled off the settee and onto the floor. Listening for a few moments in case we had woken Mum or Dad, we carried on. He unfastened my blouse and then my bra. I tried to cover myself, feeling ashamed of my skinny body and small breasts, but he cupped and kissed them with such tenderness, I overcame my unease. I unzipped my skirt and pulled it over my legs, exposing my lower half. I could feel his hardness as he pressed himself towards me. He stroked the tops of my legs where my stockings finished and slid his hands beneath my suspenders, then pulled back slightly and removed a packet from his pocket. I watched and waited, unsure, as he unzipped his trousers.

He hesitated. 'Okay?' he whispered.

I opened my arms and then my legs.

'Yes.'

Sliding his trousers down, he knelt before me and opened the packet. He placed a condom over his erection. It was the first time I had seen one and couldn't believe how they grew. He rolled the thin rubber down to the base of his shaft as he moved towards me. I slid my briefs down over my thighs. Gently, he urged himself into me, increasing the pressure as he held me firmly, kissing my neck and throat.

I placed my arms around his back and neck, and clung to him, moving with the same rhythm, as if I had no control over my movements. I didn't know what I was doing really; I suppose it was what came naturally. I opened my eyes. His hair had fallen over his forehead. His urgency increased and my body filled with a tremendous desire and need. I knew then that I loved this man more than life itself. I wanted to look after him, cook for him, wash and iron for him, sew and mend for him and have his children.

26

With much regret, I removed my pin-up photos from the attic walls, stripped off the wallpaper and re-papered the room with aeroplane-covered paper. Ian was nearly eight years old. Mum said he had to have a bedroom of his own, and I would have to share with Jo. Neither of us was happy with the arrangement, but Jo no longer wanted Ian in her bedroom. She had started her periods and wanted privacy.

We were together again in the small back bedroom and we argued over wall space. I didn't want to see images of Cliff Richard and she didn't want to see Elvis Presley pictures. We made a truce and kept them in our scrapbooks.

* * * *

I celebrated my nineteenth birthday, which was actually my eighteenth, in the pub, and began working there the following week. It was difficult some nights as I didn't get home from my day job until after six o'clock and had to be at the pub for seven thirty. On the days I worked late at the shop, I went straight from work to the pub.

I loved working with John and soon adapted to pub life. I never neglected my day job though. On Saturday mornings, as there were fewer prescriptions, I applied make-up to brides-to-be. Word soon got around locally, and almost every Saturday, some girl would come to the shop for me to apply make-up for their special day.

* * * *

It was the week before Christmas, and a quiet night in the pub.

'Do you fancy going to Skegness on holiday in the summer?' John asked one night.

'Try stopping me. When?'

'Whenever. A chap who works at our place has a caravan, says I can have it. That's if you want to go?'

Alone together for two weeks, I couldn't wait. I gave him a big hug.

It didn't take long to clear away the glasses and clean the tables. It was a horrible night; freezing fog and sleety rain. I tucked my arms around John as we waited in the queue at the chippy.

'You're going Hillsborough way, aren't you, John?' asked Keith Betts, one of the regulars. He turned and looked at John. 'Any chance of a lift?'

'Is that old Creeky back there?' said Brian Carter, at the front of the queue, shaking liberal amounts of vinegar on his fish and chips.

'There's only room for six,' John replied, as we moved up a place in the queue.

'Great, we'll wait outside.'

We left the chippy to find six people waiting beneath the canopy.

'I can't get you all in,' said John as we dashed across the car park. The others followed.

'Come on, John, you can get us all in,' said Keith. He began climbing into the back of the car as soon as John unlocked the doors.

'You'll not see us walk on a night like this, eh?'

Five people, with fish and chip packets, clambered into the back and seated themselves on each other's knees. Three were in the front, with me in the middle, our fish and chips packet squashed to my chest.

'Come on, John, hurry up. Me chips are getting cold,' laughed Keith, as John switched on the lights. They looked dim. He tried to start the engine, which turned but wouldn't fire. He tried again, nothing. Loud moans came from the back seat passengers. John got out and removed the starting handle from the boot. He placed it in the slot at the front, gave it a couple of turns and the engine fired.

'Hooray!' Everyone cheered. John gave the car a few revs, replaced the handle, and got back in the car.

'It's a bit icy,' John said, as he drove out of the car park and onto the empty road. We had only gone about five hundred yards, downhill, towards a bend, when another car came towards us in the centre of the road. John saw it, braked and tried to steer out of the way. The car skidded, spun round and crashed into the oncoming car.

* * * *

John looked around. 'Is everyone okay?' He opened the car door.

Stunned, shocked. Fish and chips everywhere. Silence.

'We'd better scarper,' said Keith Betts, as he scrambled out. 'The coppers'll be here any minute.'

The others checked themselves for injuries, and followed him, running off down the road after salvaging what was left of the fish and chips. I sat in the car while John went over to speak to the other driver. The other car, being a lot smaller than ours, was in a far worse condition.

'You should have been on your side of the road,' I heard John say, his voice raised.

'Don't blame me – you were coming down the hill too fast.' The driver replied, waving his arms and pointing.

They were still arguing when the police arrived, along with an ambulance, lights flashing and bells ringing. The driver's passenger, who didn't appear to be injured and walked to the ambulance, was taken away. A large bump was forming on my forehead where it had hit the dashboard. Chips were stuck in my hair and a mixture of fish and chips had somehow dropped down the front of my blouse. I refused hospital treatment, and wouldn't leave John. One of the policemen threw a three-penny bit on the ground and told John to pick it up, and then told him to walk a straight line. Satisfied, he took a statement, and we sat back in the car, huddled together, as the heater no longer worked. Eventually the tow trucks came for the cars, and John and I were taken home in the police car.

* * * *

While John's car was being repaired, we had to travel by bus. John was worried about the outcome of the crash and reckoned they would throw the book at him.

'But it wasn't your fault. If the other chap hadn't been on your side of the road, you wouldn't have swerved, would you?'

'Jackie, the other chap was an off-duty police officer. I don't stand a chance.'

'But surely the police who arrived on the scene could see who was at fault?'

He smiled and shook his head, pulled me towards him and gave me a cuddle.

John was right. Three months later when the issue went to court, John was charged, found guilty of Dangerous Driving, fined eighty pounds, and banned from driving for a year.

* * * *

We went to Skegness for our holiday as planned, and travelled by train. The caravan was old, yet clean and comfortable. We hired a radio from the camp shop, took sandwiches, a bottle of orange squash, a couple of blankets and a windbreak, which wasn't much use against the strong East wind, and walked the short distance to the beach. Neither of us could swim, so we paddled in the edge of the sea until it got too cold, ran back up the beach and snuggled together beneath the blanket.

* * * *

We lay among the sand dunes. John was chewing on a blade of grass.

'I'm going back in the joiner's shop when we get back,' he said.

John had told me previously that he had taken an apprenticeship as a joiner upon leaving school, but after three years, had decided on the drawing office.

I rolled on my side. 'Why? I thought you happy where you were.'

'Not really,' he replied, spitting out the grass. 'More money for a start. I can work Saturday morning for time and a half and Sundays for double time. They're really busy just now.'

'But what about giving up Sunday dinner times at the pub?' I asked.

'They'll manage. There's plenty of other staff who can take my place.'

'If you sure that's what you want to do.' I shrugged my shoulders. What else could I say? We weren't married.

'I'll need the money to get another car when I get my driving licence back, and the insurance will cost a fortune.'

'You're really missing it, aren't you?'

He rolled towards me.

'Not half as much as I'd miss you.' He pulled me into his arms.

As lovely as the holiday was, the fact that John had been forced to sell the car and his beloved motorbike to pay the cost of the fine was a blow. He was lost without his wheels.

* * * *

It was awful to go home after the holiday. We had made love when we wanted, day or night, and sometimes both. Our nights together had gone and we had the added difficulties of having to rely on public transport.

It was another eight months before John got his licence back and went to look for another car. What a come down. Gone were the lovely wide bench seats of the Rover. All he could afford was an old 1953 Ford Prefect, which cost thirty five-pounds. The insurance, which was third party, fire and theft, cost a whopping thirty-seven pounds.

Still, we had wheels, even though the springs had long gone in the seats and we had to bang on the inside of the car for the indicators to pop out. The rusted foot-wells were covered with layers of cardboard, and needed changing every time it rained or snowed as our wet shoes leaked into the cardboard and turned it to pulp. We knew it wouldn't take us far, but as long as it got us around, it would suffice until his insurance level came down.

* * * *

One night, we met up with Hazel and Mick. They had been courting for two years and had decided to marry the following March, so Mick would qualify for a full year's married-man's tax allowance. They were going to buy a house at a cost of one thousand five hundred pounds, and had managed to arrange a mortgage. I was so pleased for them; they looked so happy.

A month later, Lynn and Alan came to the pub one night and told us they were also getting married in March. They were going to live with Alan's mum and dad as they had a spare bedroom. I wondered where John and I would live if we were to marry. There was no spare room at our house or John's. I then felt ashamed of myself for having such thoughts. We had never talked of marriage. We were happy as we were, apart from the nightly separations.

* * * *

Hazel and Mick's wedding was perfect, from start to finish.

'Your turn next,' she said. Mick her husband, standing by her side, grinned. She handed me her bouquet. We kissed and hugged as they clambered into their old Morris Minor, decorated with white ribbons.

'Goodbye all, and thanks for everything,' they called and then departed for Blackpool on their honeymoon.

Much later that night, when we had made love on our settee after Mum and Dad had gone to bed, we lay in each other arms, very aware of the time.

'I'll have to go,' John said, as he pulled away from me and put his trousers on.

'I hate this when you've got to go,' I said, as I dressed.

John straightened his shirt and reached for his jacket.

'We could get married, and then I wouldn't have to go…that's if you want to?'

I couldn't see his face. It was too dark, and he was bending over, fastening his shoes.

I switched on the reading lamp and looked at him as he straightened up, my eyes straining with the sudden light.

'You're serious?'

He combed his hair. It immediately flopped forward and he pushed it back. *James Dean.*

'Well, if you'd rather not…'

I pulled him towards me and kissed him, then I held him so tight, I couldn't breathe.

'You know I will. I love you.'

'I love you too. That settles it then. We'll get engaged at Christmas.'

I hugged him again.

'How many babies shall we have?' I pressed my head into his chest and he wrapped his arms around me.

'That's up to you – as many as you want. I'll be happy to oblige.'

'Let's have six. I can't wait.'

'Why stop there? Why not raise our own football team?'

* * * *

We were in the kitchen when we told Mum. She was delighted. She had always loved John and insisted he was too good for me.

'You'd better go and ask Charlie,' she said to him. 'He's in the front room.'

248

Mum and I let John see Dad alone. We waited in the kitchen, wondering what they were saying. He seemed to have been gone an eternity.

'What did he say?' I asked when he came back.

'He said I needed my head examining.'

'What are you laughing at?' asked Jo, as she came inside and wafted away the smoke from my cigarette.

We told her the good news.

'Good. Does that mean I'll have the bedroom to myself?' she replied.

* * * *

We went to the jeweler's: Leslie Cass, on Surrey Street. For my engagement ring, I chose a solitaire diamond in a raised platinum setting, with four tiny diamonds in the corners. My wedding ring, chosen at the same time, was a wide gold band, laid away with a deposit and a promise of further regular payments.

It was my best Christmas ever. I was so proud of my engagement ring. I even stopped biting my nails, well, for a few weeks. I was deliriously happy, in love, and buying things for my bottom drawer.

27

We found somewhere different to go on our evenings off. A pub called The Crown Inn, which was next door to Stones' Brewery, or Cannon Brewery, as the oldies preferred to call it. It was a lot smaller than the Five Arches, having just a lounge and taproom but no concert room. A jolly, elderly couple who were always laughing and telling jokes with the customers owned it.

'It must be my good looks that bring you back,' the landlord said with a wink, as we walked in one evening. His ruddy face grinned. The lounge was quite full and the Z Cars theme was playing on the jukebox. John and I sat on two stools in front of the bar.

'Pint and a half of bitter, is it?' Remembering, he looked at John and reached under the counter for the glasses.

'Please,' said John, as he felt in his trouser pocket.

'You've been in a few times now,' the landlord continued. 'Have you come to live round here?' He pulled on the pump, his bicep rising with the effort. Placing the full pint in front of John, he began filling a glass for me.

His hair was dark and curly, with a lot of grey at the sides and slicked back. I could smell the Brylcream, which flattened the curls, creating small waves. With his Errol Flynn style moustache, he had the look of celebrity hairdresser Raymond Bessone, Mr Teasy-Weasy. I began to laugh.

'What's so funny?' he asked. His dark beady eyes sparkled. He placed the filled glass in front of me.

'It's you. You look like Mr Teasy-Weasy,' I replied. He laughed louder, and so did John, but not before tapping me on the shin with his foot.

'Hello, I'm Kitty,' said his wife, who had been serving someone else. She came towards us and opened a packet of cigarettes. 'And this is Arnie.' She looked up at her husband, who was taking a pinch of snuff. 'And don't believe anything he tells you.'

Arnie winked as she spoke. She gave him a playful slap. He sneezed and pulled a clean white hanky from his trouser pocket. The air filled with menthol. She too, had a kindly face, with lipstick applied too generously beyond the outline of her lips. Her hair was dyed blonde and set in waves and curls. The glasses she wore had pale pink, frosted bat-wing frames.

Taking out a cigarette, she placed the packet on the bar in front of John and me.

'Help yourselves.' She nodded towards the cigarettes. The men refused. I took one, which she lit with a lighter similar to mine.

'Thanks. Park Drive, my favourites, how did you know?'

Kitty and I took a long drag on our cigarettes and then raised our glasses.

'Good Health,' we said, as we took a drink.

'So, what brings you round here?'

'Nothing, really. We like trying different pubs on our nights off. We work up at the Five Arches.'

'Oh really,' Kitty replied, placing her cigarette in the ashtray as she went to refill someone's pint. 'Arnie, the mild's gone,' she shouted as she pulled on the spluttering air-filled pump. Arnie immediately made his way down to the cellar.

'Not be a minute,' she said to the customer, and took a quick drag on her cigarette. 'Can I be getting you anything else?'

'Aren't they nice?' I said to John. 'I wish I worked here instead of the Five Arches.'

'Yes,' he replied. 'It's smaller and has more atmosphere.'

'Do you think it's because these are owners, and Doug and Elsie at the Arches are managers?'

'That shouldn't have anything to do with it, but maybe you're right.'

Arnie came up from the cellar, mopping his sweat-covered brow. He placed a bucket on the beer tray and drew on the pump until the amber liquid settled and cleared.

'There you are, love,' he said to Kitty, and took the bucket away.

'More beers?' Arnie asked, when he returned and saw our near-empty glasses.

'Yes, please,' said John reaching in his pocket for some money.

'I'll get these,' said Arnie, and felt in his pocket. He placed some money in the till and gave me two shillings. 'Put some music on, love.' He looked towards the jukebox.

I slid off the stool. 'What do you want on?' I asked.

'Anything you want. It's all noise to me,' he laughed.

'Is there anything you want on, Kitty?' I asked as she joined us.

'Yes, love, Burl Ives – *Little Bitty Tear*. Brian from the vending company has been today and changed the records.'

I read the new selections. Burl Ives had finished his song of woe before I'd chosen my selection. I returned to the bar, as B. Bumble and the Stingers belted out *Nutrocker*, which thundered around the room. Arnie jumped back, clutched his chest and laughed.

'Give over, you daft bugger,' said Kitty. 'You'll be doing it once too often.'

We talked some more when they weren't serving customers, and John ordered another round. Suddenly the outer door burst open and a man with a London accent rushed in.

'Watcha, cock. Are you the landlord?' He looked at Arnie.

'I was when I got up this morning,' Arnie replied.

'I've twenty-seven thirsty, hungry football supporters outside – our coach has broken down and…'

Before anyone could answer, a crowd of supporters, swinging wooden rattles, chanting 'Fulham won,' and wearing black and white football scarves stormed through the doorway.

The seated regulars stood up.

'What's going on?' they shouted, picking up their drinks, while those at the bar jostled with the newcomers.

'Hey watch it!'

'Who're you shoving?'

''Ere, watch it mate.'

'Gawd' struth,' said the driver, as the noisy supporters pushed their way to the bar and the toilets.

Arnie banged on the bar with a baseball bat he'd pulled out from under the counter. The driver raised his hands, moving them up and down.

'Shhh, shush,' he said.

Between the driver and Arnie, they quietened the crowd.

Arnie's face reddened, and sweat poured from his brow as everyone turned to look at him.

'Listen to me. If you'll all quieten down, you'll all get served, and Kitty here will see what pies we've got.' The crowd cheered. Kitty looked daggers at Arnie and then looked across at me and shrugged.

'Pies, what pies?' she mouthed, and pulled a face.

Arnie rapped on the counter again. 'And be of mind – we close at ten o'clock.' The crowd booed. 'Now, what can I get you?' he asked the man nearest to him.

Kitty looked anxious as she made her way to the pie oven, leaving Arnie to attend the thirsty crowd. John and I had moved out of the way when the crowd came in. Standing at the top end of the bar, we looked at each other and nodded.

'Arnie, can John and I give you a hand?' I asked quietly. He was pulling a pint and checking the head. He adjusted the sparkler, and the beer pulled flatter.

'Southerners, they don't like it with a head on.' He looked up. 'Sorry, love, did you say something?'

'I said – do you want us to give you a hand?'

'Don't you think I'd look odd with three?' he joked. 'Wouldn't mind at all. I'm sure you'll be a big help.' He placed the pint on the counter and opened the hatch on the bar-top for John and me to get through. John took off his jacket, placed it on a stack of crisp boxes, and began serving. Arnie finished serving the driver.

'Cor, blimey, mate. Thanks for that, guv,' he said, and handed over a ten-shilling note. 'An' get yourself one, and the missus, an' the young 'uns.'

'Have I to help Kitty or serve?' I asked Arnie.

'If Kitty can manage, you can help serve.' More pints splashed onto the counter.

Kitty took some pies out of a cupboard and stood them on an oven plate. 'I've only got eight hot ones – the rest are cold and will take twenty minutes to warm up. I've put the peas on to heat, and the gravy. Do you want to take the orders?'

'I'll have a pint and a night with the barmaid,' one of the supporters said, as I appeared at the counter. 'I was here first,' said his pal, as he pushed to his side. 'Cor, they've got some right stuff up here, eh Nick?' he said, eyeing me up and down.

Arnie was watching as he served. He nudged John, who was working by his side on the other pump. 'They're chatting your bird up.' He looked over as I took the comments and compliments in good part.

'That's all right, Arnie. Jackie can look after herself. She's used to it, gets it all the time at the Five Arches.'

'I'm not surprised,' I heard Arnie reply, and saw him wink at John.

I looked towards the hungry men.

'Right, who wants pies?' I shouted.

They surged forward. The replies were deafening.

* * * *

At ten o'clock, when Arnie rang the bell for closing, everyone who required food had eaten. The "Four–One" chants had ceased and the Fulham supporters were offering commiserations to the defeated Sheffield Wednesday supporters.

Kitty and I lit up a much-needed cigarette, and John began

collecting the empty glasses. At half-past ten, the driver announced that the coach was roadworthy. After giving thanks and warm handshakes for our hospitality, the supporters were on their way back to London. Shortly afterwards, when the tables, plates and glasses were all cleared away, we sat having a drink.

'So much for having a night off,' Kitty said to us, as I took a couple of cigarettes from my packet and handed her one. 'We're very grateful, Jackie.'

'Couldn't see you struggle, Kitty. It's not every night you get a coach party in.' We inhaled deeply on our cigs and exhaled into the smoke-filled room.

'How much do they pay you at the Five Arches?' Kitty asked, spreading her hands on the bar-top and looking at her manicured fingernails.

John and I exchanged glances.

'Half a crown an hour,' I replied.

'Well, how would you like to work here, for three shillings an hour?' She looked up and smiled.

John and I didn't know what to say.

'Five nights a week, seven-thirty till ten thirty?' she added.

I did the maths in my head. That was an extra seven and six a week – each.

Two weeks later, we started our new positions.

28

'You're what? Emigrating? Why?' I was visiting my cousin Brenda and her husband Len's home in Pitsmoor. Auntie Doris had said they wanted to see me.

'Len doesn't like it around here anymore. Says if we don't move soon, we'll be the only white people left. We can go on the £10 assisted passage.' Brenda whispered, as if the neighbours might hear. 'There are too many coloureds moving into the area. I don't mind them, but Len can't stand them. Lazy Bs, he calls them.'

'But they don't cause any trouble, do they?' I asked, and took a piece of cake from one of Brenda's best china plates.

'Don't tell me you've forgotten about the East House pub shootings a couple of years ago.'

'Sorry, Brenda, I had.'

'Len says it not safe around here anymore. Different culture, says they breed like rabbits, bring the property prices down, and he doesn't want our kids growing up with them.' She poured more tea into our cups.

'I'm surprised at Len. He hasn't always thought like this, has he?'

Brenda's lips tightened as she thought about it.

'Yes, I suppose he has, but he's never been this angry as of late.'

The door opened and Len walked in. He went over to Brenda, kissed her on the cheek and looked across at me.

'Hello Jackie – where's John?' He took off his shoes and put his carpet slippers on.

'He's working. Double time for Sundays,' I replied. I opened a packet of cigarettes and offered one to Len.

'I'll stick with my own brand if you don't mind.' He turned to Brenda. 'Where's the kids?' he said, looking around the room.

'They're playing in the front room, can't you hear them?' Brenda replied and went to the cupboard for his mug.

'I hear you're thinking of going to Australia,' I said, lighting my cigarette.

'Not thinking. Going,' Len stressed, and took a cigarette out of his packet, lit it, sat down in his chair and picked up the Sunday Times.

'Australia's a long way, Len,' I said.

Brenda looked across at me, gritted her teeth and shook her head.

'We're not stopping around here anymore, that's for sure.' Len's face was red and angry as he slapped the newspaper down.

I didn't know how to reply. Whatever I said would only make his anger worse. He interrupted my thoughts by suddenly jumping up.

'Here, you're the "arty" one in the family. Come and look at this.' He took a deep drag on his cigarette and led me to the back door. 'There! Take a look at that.' He opened the door and pointed to his neighbour's house. 'Tell me what you see.'

He was shouting. Brenda called him to come back in. He stood staring at the window frame and took hold of my arm.

'Len, I don't know what you're on about.' I'd only once seen him this mad once before, when his previous neighbour, Mr Jackson, had a cat that crapped in Len's garden. Len saw it, grabbed hold of the cat and rubbed its face in the mess. He then banged on Mr Jackson's door and thrust the screaming cat, which he was holding by the scruff, into Mr Jackson's arms.

'If that cat ever shits in my garden again, I will kill it. My kids play in that garden, and if I see any cat-shit on them, or their clothing, I will kill you as well.'

I remembered it, vividly. Brenda said that Len had scared Mr Jackson so much it was the reason he sold his house and moved away. Len insisted he had deliberately sold it to a Jamaican for revenge.

'What can you see?' He brought me back to the present incident.

My eyes scanned the house next door and the piles of rubbish atop an old stained mattress, and more debris strewn across what once had been a well-tended garden. 'Is it the rubbish?'

'Yes…And…?'

'I don't know, Len. What else am I looking for?'

'What colour is that window frame?' He pointed to the upstairs window.

'Red?'

'Now look at the downstairs window. What colour is that one?'

'Green?'

'What shade of green?'

'Lime green,' I added.

'Right, now what colour is the door?' Len was dragging away on his cigarette as if someone was going to take it from him.

'Purple, with yellow panels.' I rather liked the vivid colours, but I could see what Len meant. They didn't belong on the outside of a house that was situated in a once very select area.

'Right again. Now what colour are my window frames and doors?'

I turned and looked at the house Brenda and Len had worked so hard for, and the garden with close-cut grass and a play area for the children. The colourful flower borders; the window frames and doors of the house neatly painted in white and beige.

'They'll make this area into a shanty-town before they've done, and the houses'll not be worth ten quid.' Len said, and stormed back inside.

'Calm down, Len,' said Brenda. 'And stop getting upset about it. I've said I'll go.'

'Bloody foreigners. Bongo drums playing all night,' Len mumbled, and slumped into his chair.

Brenda looked at him and shook her head.

'Jackie, we really wanted to ask you if you'd like to buy our furniture,' Brenda said.

My eyes lit up. I loved their G Plan furniture – it was so modern.

'We thought, as you're getting married, it might give you a start, especially as it's so costly to furnish a house from scratch.

'Do you mean all of it? Brenda, we'd love to, but we haven't fixed a date yet. Can I talk to John about it and get back to you?'

'We're not leaving yet – you might have fixed a date before we go. Find out how much it would cost to put it in storage – there's a place called Merrill's near where you live.'

29

'Just what we need, a bit of young blood around the place,' said Arnie after our first night. We were sitting at the bar having a drink after time had been called. Opening hours in pubs had been extended now, but it didn't make any difference – people just came in half an hour later.

The Crown was such a busy place. Surrounded by houses and steel works, the off-sales were as busy as the two bars, and required a full time assistant. Arnie had an American-style hot dog cooker installed near the off-sales counter. Made from stainless steel, it had a central container for heating the sausages. Adjoining it was another pan for the onions, and around the cooking area were twelve upright spikes for warming the bridge rolls. From evening opening time at five thirty until dark, kids came from the surrounding streets for hot dogs and bottles of pop.

We soon got to know the regulars: the rolling mills' shift workers and their break-times. Pints of beer, pulled ready and standing on the bar. The doors would open, and hot from tending the furnaces, sweat towels draped around their greasy necks, the thirsty workers rushed to the bars. Pints were downed in one gulp and money was handed over the bar for the next pint as well. The till rang constantly.

Endless plates of pie and peas vanished over the counter to hungry workers, while others shouted.

'How much are t' pies and peas, love?'

'One and six.'

'How much is t'gravy?'

'Free.'

'How much is t' bread?'

'Free.'

'Okay, I'll have a plate o'gravy wi' six slices o' bread.'

* * * *

The two rooms filled, and emptied just as quickly. Scooting around the counter, I collected the empties and washed them, ready for the next steelworks shift change.

I was happy working in either bar, the taproom or lounge. It was mostly managers and executives, living out of town, who used the lounge during the early evening. They would relax with a drink, allowing the traffic to clear before making their way home. Later, the place would fill up with locals.

John and I loved working there and the extra pay soon began to accumulate. Every week without fail, John gave me his wages from the pub, which with mine, I took to the post office and deposited into the savings account I had opened, to pay for our wedding and a deposit on a house.

I decided my sister and cousin Margaret would be my bridesmaids and they would wear blue brocade and I, although no longer a virgin, white lace. Mum would get the wedding cake from Fletchers where she worked. A three-tier heart-shaped one with blue ribbons.

Josie was concerned, as the wedding date we were planning fell in the same year as her forthcoming heart operation when she reached sixteen, and coincided with her leaving home to attend the Teachers' Training College at Bingley. We decided to carry on as we were and not fix a definite date yet.

Although we were saving hard, we still took holidays in Bridlington, Scarborough or Skegness. John's insurance was still high, which meant we could only have old cars, which were unreliable for long distance driving. We decided to risk it, and take the Austin A40 to Scarborough. The old Ford Prefect had had its day and although the Austin wasn't much newer, it didn't have cardboard in the foot wells.

It was the beginning of July, warm and sunny. Hundreds of seagulls called from the rooftops as we drove around the streets, looking for nice, clean-looking guesthouses. All displayed notices stating: "B & B 10/6 – Hot & Cold in all rooms."

'You wait in the car while I take a look,' said John.

'Why can't I have a look too?'

'No, it's best this way. Once inside, if I don't like the look of the place, I can tell them I'll just ask the wife. And then we'll drive off.'

We drove along the streets. The third B&B he chose was on a side street; with a large plaque with the name "Rosedene" above the door.

'This one's okay,' he said when he came back out, and took the suitcase from the boot. Although we had both packed a case, we pushed all our clothes and shoes into one – a married couple wouldn't have two suitcases.

I made sure my narrow Woolworth's wedding ring didn't look green, and accompanied him up the steps. Mrs Aysgarth welcomed us and immediately turned the window sign around so it read No Vacancies. She discretely checked my hand. I raised it to brush back my hair as I entered the hallway.

'Lovely rings you have there,' she remarked.

'Yes they are, thanks to my wonderful husband,' I replied, and gave John a fetching smile.

'Don't overdo it,' he whispered and began walking upstairs.

'I will need payment in advance,' Mrs Aysgarth said, holding the key to room five in her hand. 'You did say a week, didn't you?'

John stepped back down and took out his wallet. A black and white cat purred around our legs.

Mrs Aysgarth looked down at the cat.

'Ah, there you are, Puddles. Are you saying hello to our guests?' The cat meowed.

'There you are, dear, you can be going up.' She handed me the key. 'Breakfast is at nine o'clock and the front door is locked at eleven pm. Let me know if you need a late night key.'

* * * *

We stripped off our clothes and dived into bed. This was the first time in a room on our own since last year. We made love, and later, queued for the bathroom along the landing.

'Are you okay?' I said to John as we got ready to go out for the evening. He looked pale. I had never seen him look so ill before.

We left the car parked outside Rosedene and walked into town, found a café, went inside and were shown to a table with a bright yellow and orange checked plastic cover. I lit a cigarette while we waited.

'Are you sure you're all right, John? You don't look at all well.' I blew more smoke up into the already smoke-filled air.

'I'll be okay – we'll get on the beach tomorrow and get some sunshine.' He reached across the table and took hold of my hand.

There was no menu – whatever was available was printed on the paper place mats. A spotty-faced teenager chewing gum came over. She held a small pocket book close to her eyes, and a thick pencil. It could have been a crayon.

'Yea?'

I looked across at John.

'Yea?' I mimicked.

John smiled at the waitress and ordered cod and chips, who thanked him by popping a bubble.

'Same for me – please,' I emphasized.

'Bread and butter?' Pop! Another bubble.

'Yes,' we both replied.

'Tea? Mugs or cups?'

'Yes,' we replied again and left her to decide whether we wanted mugs or cups.

She finished writing on the pad in the same amount of time I could have written an essay, placed the pencil behind her ear, turned and walked away.

We held hands across the table again.

'Isn't this lovely? I can't wait till we're married with a place of our own.'

'We'll make it next year for definite, eh?' John replied.

'Two teas.' The mugs arrived within minutes, followed by a plate laden with two slices of bread scraped thinly with margarine.

Half an hour later, spotty-face came over carrying two plates.

'Two haddock and chips,' she said, placing the plates in front of us.

'No, I snapped. 'Cod and chips.'

'Ain't got none.' She stood with her hands on her hips.

'What do you mean, you haven't got none?' I stared at her.

'We don't have it.'

'Then why is it written on the place mats?' I shoved my plate out of the way and pointed to where it said cod and chips.

'It's all haddock up here.'

'Then why put it on the place mats…?'

'Get your dinner, it doesn't matter.' John interrupted.

I was causing a disturbance. John cut into the fish on his plate. Spotty face shrugged and walked away.

'I wouldn't dream of talking to my customers like that.' I was angry and he knew it.

'Don't let it spoil the night.' He smiled.

It did spoil my night, but not as much as the following morning.

30

'Mrs Aysgarth, Mrs Aysgarth!' I called, and ran down the stairs.

A couple of guests were sitting in the breakfast room reading newspapers. She must be in the back. I dashed through a doorway marked No Entry – Staff Only. An elderly chap was pricking sausages on a central table.

'Excuse me,' I said.

He wiped his hands on his apron and came around the table towards me. 'Guests aren't allowed in here,' he replied, unaware of my panic.

'I need to use a phone. My husband's very ill.'

'Well, why didn't you say so?' He moved to another doorway. 'Helen!' he called.

'What is it now, George?' an angry voice replied.

'Someone's ill…'

'Whaaat?' She came rushing through the doorway. I was drumming my fingers on the table. 'What's the matter?' She clenched her hands together as she saw my agitation and came towards me.

'It's my husband, John – he can't breathe and he needs a doctor.'

She followed me as I rushed upstairs and into room five.

'Good Grief,' she cried. 'He needs more than a doctor.' She turned and rushed back downstairs.

John had been in bed when I left him, but now he was slumped over a chair by the open window, his head on the sill, breathing with difficulty, his face the colour of a storm-filled sky.

* * * *

Ten minutes later, which seemed more like an hour, an ambulance arrived. A medic placed an oxygen mask on John's face. Another medic gave him an injection, and took his pulse rate and blood pressure. When John's colour returned to near normal, they helped him downstairs and into the ambulance. Mrs Aysgarth came rushing down the steps.

'Here, take this.' She handed me a small card as I climbed into the ambulance. It had the house address and phone number on it. 'I'll pack your case for you. Ring me,' she added, as the ambulance doors closed.

The vehicle pulled away and I noticed the sign in the window had been turned, and read "Vacancies".

* * * *

'Cats?'

'Yes, cats,' said the doctor as he looked at the egg-sized swelling on John's forearm. 'A severe allergy, too,' he added.

We were in the Outpatients' department of the City General hospital in Sheffield. It was two weeks since we had left Scarborough. John had just had an asthma prick-test – his arm injected with common allergens. Of the six tests, only one was severe: the one for cats.

John told the doctor that he'd had asthma as a child but outgrew it when he was thirteen. They had never kept any pets, but his two sisters suffered with asthma, one of them very severely.

'It's going to be a life-changing position for you, John,' said the doctor. He was still watching the red lump on John's arm. 'You're going to have to keep away from cats in future, unless you want another attack like the one in Scarborough.'

'Not likely,' John replied. 'Once is enough. I'm thankful the ambulance came as quickly as it did.'

'You won't be able to avoid cats all the time, John. Eventually, you will encounter them again.'

John looked worried. 'Is there anything I can do?'

'Yes, I'm going to prescribe Sodium Cromoglycate capsules for you.'

'That's a mouthful,' John replied.

'It's all right, you don't have to take them, you inhale them.' The doctor smiled. 'The brand name is Intal Spincaps, if that's easier for you.' He took an inhaler and some capsules out of the drawer and showed John how to use it.

'Carry this with you at all times. If you ever think you're going into the proximity of a cat, place one of the capsules into the inhaler; give it a twist, and a small blade in the base will pierce the capsule and release the powder. Place the mouthpiece between your lips and inhale with a deep sucking breath. This action will coat your lungs with the powder and prevent an asthma attack. Better still, in future it would be wise to ask the proprietors if any cats are on the premises.' He raised his eyebrows as he stared at John. 'And avoid.'

John looked across at me and gave a deep sigh. I knew he was thinking of his sister and was worried that he would become an invalid too.

'Is there anything else, Doctor?'

'No, John, but you will have to be monitored regularly. I will write to your family doctor and he will get in touch with you in due course. Meanwhile, enjoy yourselves. You have an attractive young lady here whom I assume takes most of your attention.' He looked across at me and smiled, then turned to John. 'I'd like to see you again in three months' time. The nurse will make you an appointment.' He stood up and opened the door. We followed the nurse into the reception area.

We hardly spoke on the way back. John dropped me off at the shop before returning to his place of work.

'I'll see you tonight. Pick you up at quarter past seven.' He blew me a kiss and then drove down the hill. Mr Fox and Doreen both wanted to know how he had got on at the hospital. So did Mum and

Dad, when I went home that evening.

John was still quiet when he called for me later. I kissed him on the cheek as I stepped into the car. He drove off to the Crown.

'What is it, John? Something's bothering you.'

He didn't take his eyes off the road.

'Nothing,' he replied.

'There is, John. I've known you long enough to know when something's amiss. Is it because of the asthma attack?'

'I'll tell you later,' he said as he gave me a quick glance, changed down a gear and turned the indicator knob.

'Give your side a thump, Jack,' he added, as the left turn indicator stuck inside again.

* * * *

It was another busy evening in the Crown. We didn't leave until eleven -thirty, and John was still quiet. He pulled up outside our house.

'Now are you going to tell me?' I asked.

He switched off the engine and pulled me towards him.

'I don't want you to leave me, Jack,' he spoke softly, barely a whisper.

'What on earth makes you think that?' I looked him straight in the face. 'Eh?'

'You know, what if I end up like our Mary?' He looked away.

'Don't talk daft.' I turned his head towards me. 'Listen to me. You'll not get like your Mary. Mary's been ill all her life. You've had this one incident and if you do what the doctor says, it may never happen again.'

He didn't reply. He continued looking through the windscreen.

'Look how often I have chest infections and bronchitis? I still bounce back.'

He turned to face me.

'But Jack, you wouldn't want me if I was ill all the time...'

'Stop it.' I took hold of his hand. 'I don't want to hear any more.'

'I see how the other men look at you, Jack. You could have any of them.'

'John, I don't want any of them. I only want you, fit or ill. A year from now, we'll be taking our vows for better or worse – in sickness and in health.'

He gave my hand a squeeze. I pulled him towards me and held him tight, while stroking his hair.

'I'll always love you and no one else,' I said.

He looked up and gave me a faint smile.

'Look John, I've got to go. I've a blinding headache and it's that time of the month. I'll be glad when we're married and I can go on the pill. They say it helps if you're prone to heavy periods.'

We kissed, long and deep.

'I'll see you tomorrow,' I said, and slipped out of the car.

31

John's oldest sister Anne did us a big favour. She moved out to live with her friend and said we could have her bedroom. It was only small with a single bed, but ideal for newly-weds. John's mum said it would make no difference to her, so long as she could have the two-pound and ten shillings board that Anne paid. This helped John and I tremendously, as we would no longer be under pressure to buy a house before getting married.

The wedding plans were well under way. We'd originally chosen Saturday the eighteenth of September, but as there was to be a local derby football match between Sheffield Wednesday and Sheffield United on that date, we changed it to the twenty-fifth, when Sheffield Wednesday would be playing away, which also meant the choirboys would be available.

There was less than a mile distance between the church and the football ground, and I lived half way between. Both teams were in the first division, which attracted large crowds. If we'd stuck to our original date, we would have had to inform the police, so they could prevent match traffic from blocking the street as the wedding cars needed access.

We asked the vicar if we could have the bells rung. He said, no, as due to lack of funds and the state of disrepair, ringing the bells would most likely bring down the bell-tower. We were holding the reception at the Crown where we worked, and Arnie and Kitty were providing the buffet as a wedding present.

* * * *

Jo had completed all her pre-tests and was due for her operation. She left early one morning for the City General Hospital and was admitted to ward 8a. Mum, who accompanied her, stayed at the hospital throughout the day.

Dad, Ian, and I went to visit her later in the evening. Although no visitors were allowed on the ward, we could see through the circular glass windows in the doors. Jo lay asleep, connected to various pieces of equipment via tubes and wires.

Mum and Dad watched with tears in their eyes as nurses checked on her every few minutes. Along the corridor was a small room with an old brown leather settee and chair. An electric kettle stood on a green-painted cupboard. Inside the cupboard was a small brown teapot, a half-used packet of Typhoo tea, some sugar and a teaspoon in a white pot basin, along with two chipped white cups. A well-thumbed Bible was in a bedside table drawer.

Mum and Dad stayed overnight and I took Ian home.

* * * *

The following morning, Dad caught the early bus from the hospital, came home and told me Jo had been comfortable overnight. He changed his clothes and went to work. I took Shep on her morning walk, went back home, fed her, and called Ian.

Ian was being a real pain. He was refusing to wear a suit for the wedding and have his hair cut, which looked a mess.

I called him again.

I had always cut it for him, but now, at almost eleven years old, he definitely had a mind of his own. His following of Mick Jagger, Manfred Mann and The Kinks didn't help. He laughed when I told him that they used styling products on their hair to give them that messy look and that there was no comparison between their hair and Ian's messy bird's nest.

I called him again.

Ian eventually sauntered downstairs, eyes half-closed. I looked at him and his hair in disgust. His eyes opened when he saw my face.

'I'm not having it cut, so there.'

'I haven't said anything, have I?'

'No, but I know what you're thinking.' He went over to the sink to wash.

'Don't, then, if that's how you feel.' I poured myself another cup of tea. 'You'll just not be invited to the wedding.'

'Good, don't want to go anyhow.' He cupped his hands and sloshed the water around his face.

'Don't forget your ears, unless you want tatas growing out of them,' I said and lit a cigarette.

He finished washing, took the packet of Sugar-Puffs from the cabinet and sat down at the table.

'Don't you want to know how your sister is?'

'You're going to tell me anyway, so why should I ask?' He poured half a bottle of milk over the Sugar-Puffs.

'What if I said she had died during the night?'

'I wouldn't believe you because you would have come upstairs and told me before now.' He shovelled a spoonful of the puffs into his mouth.

I wanted to knock the smug grin off his face. I couldn't believe my lovely little brother had turned into such a horrible brat.

I looked at the clock: eight-fifteen. I finished my cigarette. I had half an hour to put my make-up on and get to work.

* * * *

Jo was in hospital for two weeks. When she came out, she had a scar that ran from the top of her chest, straight down the centre and turned across her lower ribs into her side. The surgeon said that the operation had been a complete success and the scar was a small price to pay for her life extension.

I listened intently to all the details of the procedure. What a position he had – how I envied him. Jo had to attend the hospital at regular intervals and continued with her studies, determined to get to Bingley College no matter what.

By the end of August, her scar had healed completely. Just the raised red line running down her upper body remained.

As the wedding was only four weeks away, I thought it was time to book the cars, flowers and the photographer, all of which I could do in my lunch hour during the coming week.

Then of course, it was the all-important wedding and bridesmaids' dresses. We arranged to go into Sheffield the following Saturday, after I had finished work at one o'clock and cut Dad's hair.

The Friday before my wedding dress shopping trip, I withdrew thirty pounds from the post office savings account and then went back in for another ten, just to be sure. Surely, it wouldn't come to more than forty?

Jo, Margaret and I made our way down the Moor to Maisie's Wedding shop. After looking in the window for a few minutes, we went inside. A lady wearing a smart blue skirt and jacket came over. She wore a white silky blouse with a bow made from the same fabric, which hung from the neckline.

'Can I help you?' she asked, smiling.

'Yes, I'm getting married in two weeks and need a dress and two bridesmaids' dresses, please.' My eyes danced over the partially covered dresses hanging on rails along the wall, and I couldn't wait to touch them and try them on.

She pulled back the rose-pink velvet curtain.

'Shall we choose one for you first?' she said. She pointed to a couple of chairs.

I looked at Jo and Margaret as they sat down, their eyes like mine, aglow with the sight of the beautiful gowns.

'My name is Joyce,' the woman said as she took a tape measure from a drawer in the counter.

I introduced myself and my sister and cousin, then removed my coat and stepped forward.

'Thirty-one inches, we'll call it thirty-two,' Joyce said as she measured my bust and jotted it down on a notepad.

'Nineteen,' she said, the tape measure wound round my waist, 'and thirty-two, hips.' She went back to the rail.

'White, is it?' She looked at my tummy, and then searched through the different-sized dresses. 'Any particular style?'

'I don't know. I've not tried one on before, so I don't know what'll suit. I don't want satin, though.'

Joyce lifted a few dresses from the rails and held them across her body. 'Do you want to try these?'

I nodded and followed her into the changing room, and as she hung them on the hook, I saw it.

'That one,' I said. 'It has to be that one.' I ran my hand over the lace.

'A beautiful choice, made from genuine Nottingham Lace.' She took it off the satin hanger and held the dress over her arm. A train of waterfall lace frills fell over the carpet.

I sucked in my breath, clasped my hands together and pressed them under my chin. I had never seen anything so beautiful.

'Don't you want to try it on?' She was laughing. So were Jo and Margaret as I stood there, overawed.

I removed my shoes, skirt and jumper and put them on the stool. I stood in my bra and briefs, then raised my arms for her to place the gown over my head, but then lowered them.

'What is the matter?' she said. A look of concern fell over her face. She pulled the dress towards her.

'Err…how much is it?'

Her expression changed and she sighed.

'Jackie dear, it's your wedding day. The price shouldn't matter.'

Jo and Margaret looked at each other and raised their eyebrows. I gulped and raised my arms again. She placed the dress over my head. The layers of net and tulle rustled as it slid over my body. I slipped my stiletto heels on, equivalent to the height of the ones I would wear on the day.

'The length is perfect,' said Joyce as she looked at the hem. 'We usually have to take the gowns up two to three inches on most girls.'

I turned and held my hair up on the top of my head while she zipped up the back. I stepped back into the large room with the floor to ceiling mirrors.

'Aaaw,' said Jo. She came towards me.

Margaret gasped.

'Jackie, it's beautiful,' she said, her eyes taking in all the details of the dress. I couldn't speak.

'Will you be wearing your hair up or down on the day?' Joyce asked.

I finally found my voice. 'I don't know. I never thought of wearing it up.'

I turned, looking at different reflections in the mirrors.

'Well, in my opinion, I think you should wear it up. Here, sit down.' She pushed the velvet-covered stool towards me and took a handful of hairpins from a box on the counter. She carefully looped my long hair onto the top of my head and secured it with the pins.

'There, what do you think to that?'

I shook my head, not in disappointment but in awe.

'Wait a minute, we haven't finished yet.' She took a veil from one of the drawers in the glass counter and opened it out fully. Then she took a single white open rose fixed on a comb, fastened it onto the veil, and placed it over my head. The veil was folded back, forming two layers, the lower one came down to past my hips and the front one was just over my shoulders. She lifted the top layer over the rose and my face.

'There, you look just like a Spanish Senorita with your dark features and hair took up.'

She bent down and pulled the waterfall train out along the carpet behind me. The three of them stepped back. A wisp of hair escaped and curled around my right cheek.

I couldn't believe my eyes. I looked so tall. I had never worn anything this length before, except my nightie.

No one spoke. I looked at the veiled girl in the mirror. I smiled and she smiled back. Her blue-grey eyes were accentuated with carefully applied make-up, her teeth white and straight, neck long and bared. I looked at her beautiful lace dress with its boat-shaped neckline. The single front panel body, lined with white taffeta, fitted into her tiny waist, and then flared out in an "A" line skirt. I loved how the slender unlined long lace sleeves came to a point on the backs of her hands with small loops of narrow elastic, which fitted over her middle fingers. The cuffs on her inner wrists were fastened with tiny press-studs.

'Here, hold this.' Joyce handed me a bouquet of faded plastic flowers. 'You'll get more of a natural feel for it with these,' she said.

I wasn't sure how to hold them.

'Higher, lift them higher, just above your waist,' she said, and nodded as I placed them in the correct position.

My hand rested on a spray of roses made from the same lace and attached to the left side of the bodice just above the waist. Joyce adjusted one of the mirrors so I had a perfect view of the back. The same boat-shaped neckline, the bodice tapering into the waist and the layers of lace gathered in rows all the way down the back from just below my waist, forming the train. I couldn't believe the girl in the mirror was me. I'm glad Mum hadn't come with us. She would have burst into tears if she had seen me in this.

I don't know how long I stood there before I realised they were speaking to me.

'Jackie, you must have it – it's so you,' Jo and Margaret were saying. Then the spell was broken as I wondered about the cost.

'Perhaps I ought to try something else on,' I said, removing the veil and headdress.

Joyce looked surprised.

'You won't have any extra to pay for alterations, dear, so that's a good saving,' she said as she unzipped me.

I stepped out of the dress, which stood up on its own. I watched the bodice part fold itself into the stiff skirts.

'But how much is it?' I called, while getting dressed.

I could see Jo and Margaret staring at each other, waiting.

Joyce came back over to the dressing room as I zipped up my skirt.

'There are a lot of costs involved in making a dress like that you know. Layers and layers of net, lace, tulle and taffeta. Can you imagine how many hours it takes the seamstresses to sew all those frills…?'

'Yes, but how much is it?' I cut her off, slipped into my shoes, stood up, and began pulling on my coat.

'Nineteen pounds nineteen and six,' she said, as she walked away with the dress.

Twenty quid for a dress I would only wear once? I sank back against the wall, gasped and looked up at the ceiling. I stood there for a minute or two. I could hear Joyce discussing the dress with Jo and Margaret. I had to make a move.

'I'm sorry, Joyce, but I can't afford that,' I said, as I came out of the changing room. Jo and Margaret's faces dropped.

Joyce gave me a weak smile. 'I can show you some cheaper ones if you like.' She went back over to the rail and pulled out a knee-length plain net dress. 'This one is twelve pounds nineteen and six.'

It reminded me of a ballerina's tutu. I shook my head. She took out another one.

'This one is fifteen pounds nineteen and six.'

It was similar to the waterfall one, but only had a plain back and the lace was thick and heavy.

'No.' I shook my head again.

Joyce put them away and closed the curtain, then dressed a mannequin in the window in the dress I had just tried on. Two girls were walking past; they stopped and commented when they saw it.

I looked at their faces and turned to Joyce.

'How much is the veil and headdress?'

Jo and Margaret's eyes lit up.

'I can do them both for two pounds ten shillings,' she replied, not wanting to lose a sale. 'And possibly something off the bridesmaids' outfits. What colour have you in mind?'

An hour later, we left the shop, each of us carrying a large bridal carrier. Jo and Margaret were happy with their blue brocade sleeveless dresses, and headdresses with a single blue rose. On our way back up the Moor, we called in Saxone and bought white pointed-toe shoes with three-inch stiletto heels, then caught the bus home. I had spent just under forty pounds. I wondered what Mum would say.

32

As it was Sunday, I was having tea at John's house. I had taken the bus as the car had broken down again and John was trying to fix it.

'I was talking to Mum earlier, Jackie,' Mary said. 'Al and I have got one of the new flats on the Norfolk Park estate – we pick the keys up next Monday.'

'That's soon come round, I thought you had to wait years on the housing list,' I replied.

Mabel poured more tea into my cup.

'No, not if you take one of the multi-storey flats. They're building fifteen twin tower blocks, fifteen storeys high, with a hundred and twenty-six apartments in each block.

'That's a lot,' I replied.

'Yes,' she added. 'And some maisonettes and three-bedroom Vic Hallam houses. You'll have to come over and have a look when we're in.'

'Our Harry has put his name down for one,' Mabel said as she removed my plate and replaced it with a dish of apple pie and custard.

'Have they named the day then?' I asked, as the room filled with the scent of apples and vanilla. I picked up my spoon.

'Next March,' she replied. 'After the wedding they're going to live with her grandmother until they get a flat.'

'What about you, Tom? You next?' I looked over at Tom who had left the table and sat in an armchair reading the paper.

'Not likely – women cost too much,' he replied.

'Oooooh!' I replied. 'Not as much as the horses and dogs.'

We all laughed. I scooped up the rest of the custard.

'At least you know where you stand with horses and dogs,' he replied, and winked. 'Confirmed bachelor, that's me.'

* * * *

'Why do houses have to be so expensive? We seem to have been saving for ages,' I said, one evening after looking through the evening paper.

'There's always private renting,'

'Give over, John, you saw what some of those places were like before we decided on buying, and they're asking a fortune in rent.'

'There are always the council homes,' he replied. 'Our Mary said they weren't waiting long.'

We visited Mary, Al and their son Michael after they had been in a week. Their flat was on the top level, the fifteenth floor of the highest block on the estate, Kenninghall Mount. We entered the lobby and pressed the lift button. The only lifts we had been in before were in Walsh's and Cockaynes' department stores in town.

The lift arrived straight away. We entered and pressed the button for the fourteenth floor. The lifts didn't go as far as the fifteenth floor. The machine room was inside the top of the building instead of being on the roof.

Climbing the one floor, we turned left and went to their door.

'Come on in,' said Al. 'Hope you're not afraid of heights.'

'I wasn't last time I went on the Big Dipper,' I replied as we entered.

A large storage cupboard was opposite the outer door and as we turned into the hallway, the smaller bedroom was on the right, with the large bedroom next door. The bathroom was on the left, opposite the bedroom, and the kitchen was after the bathroom, with a full-length window, which looked out onto a large terraced area. To the right was the living room. What a sight. It was enormous.

The windows were all the way across two walls and reached down from the ceiling to three feet up from the floor. On the longest wall opposite was an electric fire set in a wooden surround. On the shorter wall, a glazed door led out onto the patio.

280

'Take your shoes off,' said Mary.

'Sorry, I didn't realise,' I said and slipped my shoes off.

'No,' said Mary. 'I didn't mean for that, it's the floor – it's under-floor heating.'

The heat penetrated my feet straight away.

We walked over to the windows. Far down below were the car parks, with miniscule cars that looked like matchbox toys. Looking further, the park itself; trees and bushes just starting to shed their leaves, apart from the evergreens. You could see the wide walkway surrounding the central grass and play areas. Beyond the park, you could see the whole city and surrounding areas, stretching over the other six hills. What a view.

* * * *

The following night was our night off from the Crown, so we decided to have a night down Hillsborough. John ordered the drinks while I put some money in the jukebox. Within a minute, Gene Pitney's voice filled the room: *Looking through the eyes of Love*.

I pressed the buttons for The Ivy League and the Fortunes' new records, and sat down.

'I can't get over the view from Mary and Al's flat – it's so beautiful and modern,' I said to John.

'It sure was something,' he replied.

I waited a few minutes, listening to the records.

'John, I've been thinking.'

'So have I.'

I was surprised. 'What about?'

'No, you go first.'

'No, you go first,' I laughed and lit a cigarette.

John remained quiet.

'Okay, then.' I blew a smoke ring up to the yellow-stained ceiling.

'What if we…?' I watched his face for some reaction. '…If we were to put our name down on the housing list for a flat like Mary's?'

His eyes widened. 'Do you know something? I've been thinking the same thing.'

'Honest?'

'Of course, honest!' he replied. I grabbed hold of him and gave him a hug.

We remained silent for a minute, both of us evaluating the situation. Then we both started chattering at the same time.

'We could buy a decent car with the money we've saved,' I said. 'Besides, how would we find time to modernize a house if we buy one? We're working full and part-time.'

'We'll also be better off financially. A mortgage would cost us five pounds a week, plus rates, whereas the rent is only two pounds ten a week, and that includes rates,' said John.

'And we'll not have long to wait. I phoned the housing department today and they said about eighteen months for a two-bedroom high-rise flat.'

We sat quietly again, digesting it all.

* * * *

We told our parents, who were disappointed with our plans and said we were being foolish, just as we'd expected. However, within the week our names were on the housing list.

As the wedding was drawing near and we had already booked a hire car, we decided to look for a newer one when we came back from honeymoon. We were the happiest couple on the planet, but our happiness was short-lived.

* * * *

It was Shep. She had collapsed. Mum rang me at work and told me that Shep had come out of her cupboard at about ten o'clock and collapsed. She couldn't get back up.

'But she was alright this morning,' I said.

'I know, she was all right on her morning walk,' Mum replied.

'Where is she now?'

'On the floor – she won't let me lift her, she just snaps at me.' I could hear Mum sobbing. I had noticed Shep going a little thin around her rear but didn't think it anything to be concerned about. She was getting old – she was seven now.

'I can't come now, Mum, the shop's very busy. I'll come down as soon as I can.'

When the shop closed for lunch, I ran all the way home. Shep looked a pathetic sight. Her shiny black coat had turned dull and flat. Mum and I knelt on the floor beside her. I tried to lift her back end, but she snapped.

'Has she had anything to eat or drink?' I asked.

'No, nothing, she turns her head when I place her bowl in front of her.'

'She needs to see a vet,' I said.

'I know, and we can't carry her, it's too far.'

Mum stroked Shep's head. Tears filled her eyes. Mine too, as we feared the worst.

'I wish they could talk, and tell us what's the matter,' cried Mum.

I put my arm around her and cried along with her.

'I've got to get back to work, Mum. Will you be alright? I'll phone John and sort something out. Don't try moving her, try coaxing her with a drink.'

* * * *

'Hello, can you put me through to the joiners' shop please,' I asked. I was back at work.

'There's no reply. Can you try later?' said the switchboard operator.

'Okay, thank you.'

I tried again after half an hour. Success.

'Hello, Mr Sawbridge? I know personal calls are not allowed, but can you give a message to John Creek, please.'

'Is that Jackie?'

'Yes,' I replied.

'He's here with me now, would you like a word?'

* * * *

I didn't sleep that night. My heart was broken. It was the third time I had seen death: the chicken at Uncle Wilf's, then Granddad, and now Shep. As I thought of her, I broke into great heaving sobs as I remembered all the good times: John taking us all into Derbyshire, Shep's love of ice cream, playing ball with her in the park. The long walks with me over the meadows, through the woods and over the common on Sunday mornings. Her false pregnancies, where she made a nest in the cupboard for the pups that never arrived. Her time had gone too soon. I held my photographs of her close to my chest and cried some more.

* * * *

The following morning, I looked in the mirror. Never before had I seen myself look so terrible. No amount of make-up would disguise my red blotchy face and swollen eyes. I could barely see out of them. My nose was blocked and my jaw seemed to move of its own accord. Mum looked the same when I went downstairs, and so did Jo. Ian was quiet; he too had been crying. I didn't see Dad, he had left before I got up. We hugged each other and cried again.

'Never again,' Mum sobbed. 'Never again, it's like losing a child.'

'She was a child, Mum, our child.'

I left her with her grief and made my way to work. People I met on the way gave me weak smiles. Did they know? I tried to smile back and explain – *I've just lost my dog.* I wondered if they had experienced such tragedies. By the looks on their faces, they had. Mr Fox put his arm around me when I arrived.

'Time heals,' he said, as he patted my back.

33

It was the Sunday before the wedding and John and I were in church, but not by choice. Everything else was arranged and going to plan. John had collected his suit from the tailors and the ring from the jewellers. The white Vauxhall 101 estate had been booked to take us on honeymoon to Torquay. Our car wouldn't have made it as far as Chesterfield.

My head was aching and my throat was sore. I feared the worst. *Please God,* I said under my breath. Well, I was in church. *Don't let me get it now.* It was only September but the church was icy cold. We sat through the service, the final reading of the banns, and afterwards, the private talk with the vicar regarding marriage, the rearing of children and family values.

The following morning, my headache was worse, my nose was blocked and my chest was on fire. I went to work and Mr Fox gave me some cough medicine and said I ought to see the doctor for some antibiotics before it got worse. I said I would go after work.

* * * *

I sat in the waiting room until it was my turn.

'Next,' shouted Doctor Miller from his consulting room.

'It's my chest again.'

He took my medical history file from out of a steel cabinet of drawers and looked at the last few entries.

'Do you still smoke?' he asked.

'No,' I replied.

He raised his eyebrows.

'When did you stop?' He motioned for me to remove my blouse and cardigan so he could listen to my chest. He didn't need to, I could hear myself wheezing.

'Yesterday, when I felt this coming on,' I replied.

The stethoscope was cold on my chest.

'How many do you smoke a day?'

'Forty,' I lied, and then turned around for him to listen to my back.

He sighed and shook his head.

'I'm going to prescribe some Tetracycline tablets. Be sure to finish the course. Do you need a sick note? This is going to get worse before it gets better.'

'But doctor, it can't. I'm getting married on Saturday.'

'I am sorry, I can do nothing more. I'm a physician not a magician.'

* * * *

He was right. It did get worse, and by Thursday, I was too ill for my hen party. It made me even more miserable, knowing John had gone on his Stag night in Sheffield.

On Friday, I felt slightly better. It must have been the shock of Ian asking me to cut his hair.

'Ian, as much as I want you to have it cut, I don't feel up to it.' I gave him two shillings to go to the barbers.

He pocketed the money and said, 'I don't want to go to the barbers, he cuts it too short. You cut it long.'

'I'm surprised you can remember, it's that long since I cut it.' I was sitting in Dad's chair. I lit a cigarette. I went dizzy, coughed, saw stars and my lungs hacked and wheezed. Too soon. I flipped it out, stood up, went upstairs for my scissors, and took the towel from the hook by the sink.

'Sit down,' I said.

* * * *

Saturday morning. The skies were grey and the rain lashed down, driven by a blustery wind. Mum and Dad had risen first.

At eight o'clock, the flowers arrived and the kitchen smelled like a florists, until Dad lit his pipe. I didn't feel like eating. Nerves and a sore chest had the better of me.

I looked in the mirror: not too bad, a little bleary-eyed and pale, but nothing my make-up wouldn't cover. Mum, Dad, Jo and Ian had bacon and egg sandwiches. Mum persuaded me to have a slice of toast, which came back up within five minutes.

Margaret arrived later, her neatly-styled hair covered with a rain-mate. She took her things upstairs, then came back down and drank the tea Mum had poured for her. Mum and Dad's bedroom had a dressing table with three mirrors fixed to its top, so we used their room to get ready. Our gowns hung on the wardrobe door.

John's brother, Harry, who was best man, arrived at ten in the hire car. Curtains moved in the street as the long, sleek white car trimmed with ribbons turned around. Mum sorted out the buttonholes and sprays for their family, single white carnations for the men, and doubles for the ladies. All trimmed with maiden fern and silver paper holders.

Ian was the first to get ready. He came downstairs wearing a suit with a white shirt, a blue tie and black shoes. I looked at his hair, neatly combed and smelling of Mum's Vitapointe hair conditioner. I gave him a big hug.

'Stop it, you'll crease my shirt,' he said and struggled to break free.

I grabbed him again and gave him a big kiss on his cheek. 'I love you, little brother,' I said.

He pulled a face. 'I'll go and wait for the cars,' he said and wiped the back of his hand across his face where I'd kissed him.

'Ian,' said Mum, who was standing by the sink finishing the dishes. 'It's only just gone ten. The cars aren't coming till half past two. Go and play with that new Airfix plane you've got.'

'I can't, I need Jack to help me with it.' He turned towards me. 'Will you fix it for me, Jack?'

I glared at him. 'Yes, but NOT today.'

Dad took over the sink area and dropped his braces down by his sides as Mum dried her hands.

'You can fetch me some tobacco if you want something to do.' He turned around, his face half-covered with soapy foam and holding his shaving brush. He felt in his trouser pocket.

'Can I keep the change?' said Ian, as he took the ten-shilling note from Dad.

'No you can't, you cheeky bugger,' Dad replied and continued soaping his face.

'What kind is it?' Ian asked.

'Shag, an ounce of Shag,' Dad said as he swished the brush in the bowl.

Ian burst out laughing.

Jo, who was talking to Margaret, suddenly stopped, turned and stared straight-faced at Ian.

'What's so funny?' she said. 'Do tell.'

Ian's face turned bright red and he ran out of the house, chuckling and shouting.

'Shag, shag.'

* * * *

By midday, I had eaten a slice of toast, which stayed down. Mum cut a large pork pie into portions and placed them on the kitchen table, along with a plateful of sandwiches and a large piece of cheese, for any visitors to help themselves. The buffet at the Crown wouldn't start until around five o'clock. The kettle was full; the teapot empty and placed on the tray with the caddy, next to an odd selection of upturned cups standing on a tea towel.

* * * *

Dad wore the navy blue suit in which he'd married Mum. It was double-breasted with wide lapels. Ready and waiting, he sat in the front room, smoking his pipe and watching the sport on TV.

Mum's outfit was an olive green costume. The waist-length Crimplene jacket had a roll-collar with matching fabric-covered buttons, and a small mink brooch fastening on the neckline. The matching skirt was straight, mid-calf length, with a kick pleat at the back. Her matching hat, which sat on the back of her head, was small, with two long pheasant feathers. I didn't like it, probably because it was green, and reminded me of Robin Hood. I didn't say anything as, she loved it. Her shoes were plain black extra-wide court shoes to accommodate her distorted feet, acquired by wearing any-sized shoes as a child. They would be killing her before the day was out.

Ian was now in the front room, reading a comic and eating a packet of Spangles.

Jo and I went upstairs to get ready while Margaret went across the yard to the toilet.

'Thanks for being my sister,' Jo said, and wrapped her arms around me. A sob came in my throat. I couldn't reply. Jo never failed to amaze me with her timing. 'I love you just as much as Mum, Dad and Ian.'

'And I love you too,' I managed to say. I pulled away from her and held her hands. 'Don't make me cry, Jo,' I said, as I wiped my eyes. 'Not today, please.'

We both sniffed and laughed.

Margaret returned and I applied the bridesmaids' make-up, helped them to dress, and fastened the blue rose headdresses firmly into their hair. All they had to do now was to put on their new shoes, which they hated. Being five years my junior, they were not accustomed to wearing stiletto heels. They sat on the bed in the back bedroom, applying varnish to each other's nails. I couldn't wear any. Although I'd stopped biting them, my nails weren't long enough for nail polish.

Alone, I sat at Mum and Dad's dressing table and carefully applied my make-up.

My wedding underwear, neatly wrapped in white tissue paper, was in a shoebox. I'd peeped inside it every day. I carefully unwrapped the lacy lingerie and placed it on the bed.

Cutting the 32A label from the white lace bra, I put it on, followed by a pair of matching briefs and a suspender belt, then rolled the fifteen-denier nylon stockings up my legs, taking care not to ladder them, and fastened them to the suspenders. I looked in the mirror. Something was missing. Up-tipping the shoebox, the blue lace garter with one tiny pink satin rosebud, which Mum had bought, fell onto the bed. *Something blue.* I placed it high up on my left leg.

I lifted my dress off the hanger, stood it on the floor and stepped into it. *Something new.* I slid my arms into the sleeves, fastened the cuffs then shouted for Jo to come and fasten the zip.

Mum shouted upstairs.

'Brenda and Len's arrived – they're just having a cup of tea.'

Len was giving me away. It was Dad's suggestion. It's not that he didn't want to – but he had been having dizzy spells and with his chest in poor condition, couldn't stand for long periods. He was now seventy-six, and still working. I understood, and didn't want to put him under any stress. Len was my only adult cousin and the perfect choice. I had so many uncles; it would have been unfair to single one of them out.

It was the same with choosing my bridesmaids. I had so many cousins, I couldn't have them all, so I chose one. As Auntie Doris had been a second mother to me, I chose her youngest daughter, Margaret. Talk of the devil.

'Doris is here,' shouted Mum.

'Let me look at you!'

Auntie Doris came running upstairs, shouting. She burst into tears.

'Come here, love, you look wonderful.' She pulled me into her arms, hugged me tight to her chest, then stepped back while holding my hands. 'Well who'd have thought it? Our little Jack-a-leen all grown up and getting married.' Her eyes filled again.

290

'Don't,' I said, 'I've got mascara on and it'll run,' I laughed and cried at the same time, then coughed.

'You'll catch your death – the weather's awful out there.' She pulled at the front neck of my dress and looked down. 'Haven't you got a poultice on?'

'No, Auntie Doris, I don't want one on,' I said.

'I'll go and make you one. It'll not be seen under your dress. You'll thank me for it one day.' She went downstairs, her bright orange curls bouncing around her head.

Mum came up with a cup of tea and one of my tablets. Her eyes filled with tears as she placed the cup of tea on the mantelpiece.

'Don't you start,' I said, as I gave her a hug. 'I'm going to have to re-do my mascara.'

'You look beautiful,' she said. 'And I wish you much happiness. You've a good man there, look after him. I know he'll look after you. He's promised me and Charlie that.'

'The photographer's here,' shouted Auntie Doris and she came running back upstairs. I could smell the kaolin.

I let go of Mum's hand.

'I don't want it on,' I pleaded. 'Tell her, Mum.'

'You can take it off later,' Mum whispered and unfastened my zip. The front of my dress fell forward.

'There, that's got it,' said Auntie Doris as she slapped the hot poultice across my chest, securing it with strips of zinc-oxide tape.

Mum re-fastened my dress. Jo and Margaret came into the bedroom.

'The photographer's here, Jack,' they said.

'I know and I haven't put my veil on yet.' I scooped my hair up, and secured it with hair grips and pins. The green brooch was on the dressing table and I tucked it into the back of my hair and fixed it in place. *Something old.*

I pushed the comb of the headdress with the single white rose into the top of my hair and shook my head. It was firm. Then I pushed the wires of Brenda's pearl drop earring into my ears.

Something borrowed. The smell of the poultice wafted up as I sat down, checked my mascara and re-applied my lipstick. Jo sprayed me with Blue Grass perfume.

There. Ready. Jo stood to my left and Margaret to the right. They were wearing their blue brocade dresses and silver heart-shaped locket necklaces I had bought for this special day. The three of us looked into the mirrors and smiled. At least fifteen faces smiled back.

* * * *

'Hold that pose,' said the photographer as he came into the room. His camera flashed.

'The cars are here!' shouted Ian. My heart skipped a beat. I raised the front of my dress as I stepped into my shoes. Jo and Margaret carried theirs as we all went downstairs. The photographer followed.

'I'll see you at the church and hold onto your veil,' he said as he left.

I looked out of the window at the two black limousines trimmed with white ribbons, the seats covered with white sheets. The butterflies in my tummy awoke.

Neighbours began appearing in windows, doorways and entries.

Brenda and the children had already left to meet other relatives waiting in the church. Mum, Dad, Auntie Doris and Len, with their buttonholes and sprays pinned in position, stood waiting. Jo and Margaret were holding their posies close to their chests. I took a deep breath as they stared at me as if it was the last time they would see me. Dad dabbed his eyes with his hanky, then gave me a gentle hug, afraid of crushing my dress.

'Thanks Dad, for everything.'

A uniformed usher came inside. The butterflies fluttered.

'Can we have passengers for the first car please?' He held the door open.

Mum, Dad and Auntie Doris went outside, the women holding on to their hats. Dad's tie whipped over his shoulder. They waved to the neighbours and disappeared into the car, which slid silently out of the street.

The usher came back into the house. The butterflies danced. 'Bridesmaids next,' he said, as the second car moved forward. He escorted Jo and Margaret to the waiting car. They held on to their headdresses as they teetered on their heels. Ian followed and the usher closed the door and stepped back inside.

'Won't be long before the first car's back,' he said. 'It has its advantages, living near to the church.'

He left me alone with Len. I went into the kitchen, removed the poultice from my chest and threw it into the pedal bin. Lifting my bouquet from the table, I took a deep breath, and thought of the happy and sad times we'd had as a family.

The fridge rattled and shuddered to a stop. I listened to the unfamiliar silence, apart from the wind howling through the ill-fitting door and window frames. Even the steelworks yards were quiet. A distant cheer came from the reserve match at the football ground.

I stood and looked around my home of the last seventeen years. The dripping tap, which caused the brown stain in the white Belfast sink that Mum couldn't remove. The clock, on the tiled fireplace, set in a small imitation ship's wheel, which Dad wound every week. It had ticked away the minutes, hours, days, weeks and years of my childhood. I turned around and looked at the bellied walls I wallpapered annually. The lino-covered floor and half-moon rug in front of the fireplace. Everything spotless and all so familiar, and now I was leaving it all behind. Embarking on a new life, with a husband, and eventually children, in a home of our own, which I hoped would hold as much love as this one.

Looking at the empty cupboard that had been Shep's until recently, my eyes filled with tears, and a sob rose in my throat. I swallowed and looked towards the plaster-patched ceiling, and willed myself out of my moment of sadness. I pulled a stem of Baby's Breath from my bouquet, and placed it where she had lain.

Returning to the front room, I looked at Len in his new suit and well-shined shoes. I loved Brenda and Len, and their children, and hated the fact they were emigrating next spring.

'Quick smoke before we go?' he said and pulled his cigarette packet from his pocket.

'I daren't. If I start coughing, I'll not stop. You have one though.'

'Nah, I'll wait. It's not a catholic service.' He peered through the window, and then looked back. 'There's quite a crowd. Nervous?'

The butterflies had gone. 'No, not now. Are you?'

He began shaking deliberately and then laughed.

'You look wonderful. John's a very lucky man.' He kissed me on the cheek and lifted my veil forward, then took hold of my arm and placed it on his.

My eyes misted over as I looked at the man who had taught me so many things. Chess, Crib, Solo, Rummy, Blackjack and Backgammon, and, even though I would never need such information, showed me how different metals were measured and tested, and how to blow smoke rings and smoke Capstan Full-Strength cigarettes. He even told me what was important about the Sunday Times Newspaper.

The door opened.

'Time to go,' said the usher.

Len looked at his watch and then at me. 'Ten to three – ready?' I took a deep breath and licked my lips as he escorted me to the door.

'Hold onto your veil,' said the usher as he dropped the latch and closed the house door behind us.

I waved to the neighbours as they sighed their oohs and aahs, and then stepped into the car. Len carefully lifted my train onto the seat by my side. He sat next to me and held my hand.

I felt like a queen as the ribbons flapped and the car made its way silently out of the street.

Afterword

It wasn't the fact that it was our wedding night that had ensured we didn't sleep. It was the sound of the rain lashing against the window and my continuous coughing. Instead of being in sunny Torquay, John and I were in my bed at home. There was no honeymoon for us, yet. The expensive hire car stood in the street going nowhere, apart from Bingley. Jo had to go to the Teacher Training College and John said he would take her.

I looked at my wedding dress and John's suit hung on the wardrobe doors. He had looked so handsome in his new suit, shirt and Slim-Jim tie.

I turned towards him.

'It was a lovely day, John, wasn't it?' I didn't need an answer. I loved him so much and he loved me just the same. Yesterday, in church, he turned as I came down the aisle towards him. His eyes glistened like sapphires. They spoke *I love you* a thousand times over.

The service had been very solemn until saying our vows, when John said:

'In sickness and in health,' and I had broken into a raucous cough. The congregation tried to muffle their laughter and even the vicar grinned.

I looked at the broad gold wedding band John had slipped on my finger, along with my engagement ring, and curled myself into his arms. We lay for another hour, re-living the day. We made love, which wasn't a success, owing to my coughing bouts, so we lay together, holding each other close; content in each other's arms. Our future together stretched before us. I was so very happy and so grateful to Mum and Dad for the upbringing they had given me.

Reaching under my pillow, I felt the brooch I had removed from my hair last night and squeezed it in my hand. I looked at the teddy bear sitting on top of the wardrobe, the blue ribbon long gone, his threadbare body covered with a blue cardigan I had knitted for him when I was ten.

Once again, I saw the tall dark-haired handsome man walking up the path, smiling, his forage cap tilted to one side, the khaki greatcoat flapping around his knees, and then his arms reaching out...*Thank you, Frank, for giving me to Mum.*

* * * *

There was a knock on the door and Mum came in with two cups of tea, followed by Ian.

'You don't look any different,' he said, as John and I sat up.

I was wearing the blue lace and nylon negligee Mum had bought for my honeymoon.

'Why should we look any different?' I said.

John and I looked at each other and then at Mum who opened the curtains and shrugged her shoulders.

Ian sat on the bed, and laughed.

'John's got pyjamas on,' he said, still laughing and then he looked at me. 'You're not preggars, are you?' he added.

'Where does he get it from?' I said, shaking my head, and broke into a coughing fit.

'Jack,' he said. 'If you're not going away, will you help me build the plane when you get up?'

Mum intervened.

'No, she's not going to fix the plane for you. Now get out and leave them alone.'

She ushered Ian out and followed, closing the door behind her.

What happened next?

If you enjoyed *The Girl with the Emerald Brooch*, you'll love the next exciting instalment in Jacqueline's life, *The Power of Love*.

Here's a tantalising extract from the book to whet your appetite.

The Power of Love
1975

Warm needles of light sought my closed eyes, as the long rays from the Mediterranean sun pierced the ventilation holes in the metal shutters.

I looked around in the semi-darkness. The crumpled top sheet lay beside the bed on the tiled floor, the room heady with the scent of sex. The creased and damp bottom sheet clung as I turned towards him, still in the depths of sleep. Sensing movement, he reached out. Unable to resist, I folded myself into his arms. Within seconds, his growing erection pulsed against my skin.

I had no need of foreplay; he had pleasured me enough throughout the night. I needed him. His touch, his weight, his scent, his warmth. With him, I unveiled a passion I never knew my body possessed. I pulled him onto me.

'Fill me,' I said.

* * * *

I awoke for the second time that morning. The usual all-consuming guilt washed over me as my thoughts turned to John, back home.

Someone knocked on the door.

'Servicio en la habitación.'

'Just a minute,' I replied.

'Dave, the cleaner's here. Time to get up.' I shook his shoulder.

He pulled me towards him again.

297

'No, not now.'

He grinned and tugged my hand. 'She'll come back.'

I pulled free and ran into the shower, turned it on, and stood beneath the spray of warm water.

'You don't think that's going to stop me, do you?' he said, as he pulled the shower curtain back and joined me. My heart missed a beat and the familiar thrill filled my body.

'Stop it, Dave, she'll be back in a minute.'

The broad grin spread across his face.

'Dave, I'm serious.' I laughed

'So am I,' he said, and pressed me against the wall.

'Dave…' His mouth covered mine as he lifted me onto him. The water sprayed and trickled between us.

* * * *

We were staying in the Hotel Belvedere. It was our last day in Majorca before going home. I had promised John I would finish the affair with Dave while I was away. Yet here we were, walking from the hotel, hand-in-hand like any other couple deeply in love. I was wearing a long pale ivory cheesecloth skirt with a long-sleeved matching top with a draw cord neckline, six rows of beads I had bought from the hippy market, cork wedge heel sandals with corded ankle ties and a fine long headband scarf with the ends trailing down my back. The headband was embellished with small silk flowers. My hair was long and painfully straightened.

Dave wore his wide leg flares, an open neck cotton T-shirt and suede waistcoat. With his platform shoes, his six-foot-two frame accelerated to six-five. We had loved and played all week like a couple of exuberant teenagers, unlike civilised adults now in their thirties.

We passed rows of red and purple climbing bougainvillea, clinging to everything in its path.

At a beach café, we stopped for a beer and a glass of wine. We removed our shoes and walked along the edge of the sea as it lapped onto the beach. We hardly spoke. What more could be said? Finishing with Dave would break my heart, but I owed it to John.

* * * *

We put on our shoes and continued into town and Tito's nightclub.

The meal was typical touristy Spanish fayre. Dry bread rolls, gazpacho soup, oily chicken and vegetables smothered in greasy gravy, and a slice of cake, probably made from leftover bread and sweetened with honey or sugar.

The wine was okay though. We sat with our drinks, holding hands and watched the entertainment: a juggler, xylophonist and a comedian who told the same jokes in four different languages. The singer and band were good, and we took advantage of the dance floor. I looked at the other couples, some waltzing professionally, holding their partners in perfect position. Others were like Dave and I, holding each other close, moving slightly, swaying to the strains of Scott McKenzie's *Let's go to San Francisco*, *Hang on in there Baby* by Johnny Bristol, and *Can't get enough of your love, Babe* by Barry White.

I placed my head on his chest. The week had passed so quickly and these last few precious hours would not be re-lived. A sob came up in my throat and my eyes filled with tears.

I looked up at him and knew he was thinking the same. His roguish grin, that had first attracted me to him, had vanished. He saw my tears and his chin quivered. Somehow, it didn't matter who saw us.

I looked around the room, at strangers, with their own emotions to contend with. I thought of the war films I had seen, with women dancing with their husbands or lovers, wondering if that would be their last time together.

* * * *

The airport was hot and crowded. Coaches and taxis contested for space. Frustrated drivers pressed their horns. We made our way into the terminal. Neither of us spoke. Joining the check-in queue, we presented our flight tickets and handed over our cases, then made our way to Passport Control, where our passports were dutifully stamped.

Entering the departure lounge, frustrated people were fanning themselves with whatever was to hand. The knowledgeable Spanish women carried fans.

We managed to find a quiet area and sat down.

Dave spoke first.

'Is that it, then, it's over?' He didn't look at me; he stared out of the window, watching the planes taking off and landing.

I took a deep breath.

'Dave, you know it has to be, there's no alternative.' I shook my head and clasped my hands. 'I can't put John through any more. I've hurt him enough. He loves me and…'

Dave's fiery passion welled up inside him and he turned and grabbed hold of my arms.

'But I love you, Jack.' His eyes, dark with passion and anger.

'I know, Dave, I love you, you know that, but I'm married to John and have been for ten years.'

He took his hands from my arms and burst into tears; great heaving sobs. 'I can't live without you in my life, Jack.' His tanned, contorted face pleaded.

'Stop it, Dave, I'm not enjoying this either. It's a wrench for me too.'

The public address system announced our flight. A shuttle bus transported us to the plane standing in the distance on the melting tarmac. Service personnel were busy in the blistering heat beneath the undercarriage. Waiting in turn, we climbed the steps and silently boarded the Boeing 737.

We fastened our seatbelts and listened to the safety demo. The doors were locked and cross-checked. Dave sat nearest the window, I was in the centre seat, and the seat on my other side was unoccupied.

As we taxied slowly towards the runway, the Captain informed us we were in a queue for take-off. After ten minutes, the plane swung onto the head of the runway and stopped abruptly, engines whining, holding back power.

'Are you okay?' Dave asked as he took hold of my hand.

I gave it a squeeze. 'Hmm,' I nodded.

There was a short silence. The chatter of the passengers subdued.

The roar from the engines became louder, the cabin began to vibrate and the plane pushed forward, gently and then with increasing force and accelerating speed, left the ground. The land tilted sharply beneath us, as the wheels stowed into the undercarriage.

The stewardesses remained seated as the plane tilted and banked to the left still climbing, then levelled before the engine noise faded and the plane settled into a cruise.

Twenty minutes later, the sounds of seat belts unfastening and the trundling of refreshment trolleys filled the cabin. I sat back, closed my eyes and wondered why I had allowed our relationship to go too far.

The Power of Love, coming soon.

For more information, visit my website:
https://jakc1.wordpress.com/

 Follow me on Twitter: @jakc1creek

 If you've enjoyed this book, please "like" its page on Facebook and help to spread the word:
The Girl with the Emerald Brooch.

About the Author

Jacqueline Creek (nee Campbell) was born in 1944 in Sheffield to the sound of the steelworks' hammers.

Her childhood dreams of becoming a surgeon were dashed as family commitments and responsibilities fell on her young shoulders. Unexpectedly failing her 11-plus, she went to Chaucer Secondary Modern School and left at fifteen. She found work as an assistant in a chemist's shop which motivated her to train for a position in the dispensary.

Jacqueline married at twenty one and moved away from the family home, giving her the opportunity to try a variety of jobs, which sadly, never gave her total satisfaction.

In her early thirties, fate played a hand that changed her life forever.

At the age of thirty seven in 1981, Jackie, as she was now called, started her own fancy dress business, which grew rapidly into a retail outlet and factory employing over 30 people. Supplying many other UK shops with her costumes and exhibiting at Birmingham and London, the business soon began exporting to a wider market, which subsequently gave Jackie a very different lifestyle from what she had known in the back streets of Sheffield.

Jackie had always enjoyed writing poetry, so after selling her business and retiring in 2012, she decided to develop her talents further by joining writing and poetry groups. Members encouraged her to write her life story, and after hearing her first chapter, she was presented with a Silver Quill award and interviewed by the Barnsley Chronicle and Radio Penistone.

'The Girl with the Emerald Brooch' is her first published work and she is now working on a sequel.

She lives in the foothills of the South Pennines with John, Dave and their assorted rescue dogs, surrounded by an abundance of nature and wildlife.

ACKNOWLEDGMENTS
In Alphabetical Order

Ann Hamblen – For believing in me

Anne Grange – Whose memoir writing workshop set me on my journey and for her perseverance in editing my work.

Anastasia Parkes – Who critiqued my early endeavours

Barnsley Writers Group – For teaching me how to write

Birks and Dyson's Funeral Directors – For confirming my memories of Granddads funeral

Doctor Morris and Doctor Ball – For helping me through my darkest hours

Friends and Family, old and new – For the 'Good Times' and their patience

Jackie's Novelties/Fancy Dress – My dedicated staff, who do not appear until the next book

Maureen Ryan – My Marvelous Mentor

Northern College – Staff and Friends, for their true support

Penistone (Salon) Poets – For teaching me how to write 'proper' poetry, (which I still can't!)

Philip Robinson – For finding long lost friends

Sue Chater – Who restored my confidence to stand up and speak

Walt Macreath – For my first teenage kiss x

And anyone else who made this story possible
– Thank you all.